The Individual and the Universe

THE INDIVIDUAL
AND THE UNIVERSE
by A. C. B. Lovell

Professor of Radio Astronomy in the University of Manchester,
and Director of the Jodrell Bank Experimental Station

THE BBC REITH LECTURES 1958

ILLUSTRATED

HARPER & BROTHERS PUBLISHERS NEW YORK

Contents

NOTE: *Throughout this book the word "billion" means an English billion, namely, one million million.*

List of Illustrations

Foreword

The six Reith Lectures on *The Individual and the Universe* are published here as broadcast in the autumn of 1958, and no attempt has been made to recast them. Occasional passages, which had to be deleted from the script at the last moment because of timing difficulties, have been retained. The fourth lecture on *Astronomy and the State* included some recordings of the lunar probe and of speech reflected from the moon. The appropriate passages have been removed to footnotes (pp. 67 *et seq.*), and some additional explanatory notes added in italics.

It was originally intended that Mr. Kenneth Brown of the B.B.C. should produce these lectures, and I am grateful to him for his early guidance and advice. Unfortunately illness prevented his continuation of this task, and in the late summer Mr. J. Weltman of the B.B.C. assumed this responsibility. The help and guidance which he gave exceeded by far the normal responsibility of a producer. To him and to many who

encouraged me by their interest and appreciation I am
deeply grateful.

A. C. B. LOVELL

Jodrell Bank
Cheshire
19 December 1958

The Individual and the Universe

I. Astronomy Breaks Free

It is with mixed feelings of fear and humility that I start on this task of talking to you about the universe. Humility, because we have to deal with the implications of observations which take us back to epochs of time before human beings existed. Fear, because the techniques and tools of our trade are often those which form the basis of military power. The successful launching of the Sputnik was a demonstration of one of the highest scientific and technological achievements of man—a tantalizing invitation both to the militarist in search of ever more devastating means of destruction and to the astronomer searching for new means of carrying his instruments away from their earthbound environment.

During the course of these lectures I shall describe the universe which we can study with our telescopes, both those parts of it which are near at hand in the solar system and those remote regions near the observable limit at distances of a few thousand million light years. At these distances the light and the radio waves become so weak that we cannot observe what lies beyond. These are the limits at which the astronomer as a scientist can give any information based on his scientific observations. We are then forced to inquire if this vast universe which we already observe represents the whole of what actually exists. In this connexion I shall evade the philosophical difficulties which surround the meaning of the existence of a universe which we can see only in the past. Nonetheless, it is salutary to remember that at any moment we see the sun as it existed eight minutes ago, the nearest star as it existed four years ago, and that for our nearer neighbours in extragalactic space the light and radio waves by which we study them have been travelling for millions of years and our information is that much out of date. At the limit of present-day observations our information is a few thousand million years out of date. Indeed, the study of the conditions which existed so long ago is of crucial importance to the inquiry into the origin of the universe and in speculations about its future history.

Although our instruments probe so far out into space and so far back in time we have no final answer to the ultimate problem of the conditions which existed when the universe was created, or indeed if there was an epoch measurable in human time-scales when the conditions in the universe were significantly different from those we observe today. In these considerations we pass from the realm of scientific observation to philosophical speculation, and in that respect our age is similar to all that have gone before. There is, however, one very important difference. Today our telescopes are so powerful that they probably penetrate to the limits of the observable universe. We may therefore be near the limit of our scientific knowledge of the universe as regards its extent in time and space and the cosmological implications of the observations now in progress have assumed an unparalleled significance.

In the long history of civilization the belief that the earth, our abode in space, was fixed in majesty at the centre of the universe was long in dying. Indeed, if you study the sky night after night with nothing but your unaided eyes, it is easy to sympathize with the old belief that the heavens are rotating with the fixed stars, that in a few hours the sun will rise in the east and travel across the sky. Yet only three centuries ago men were persecuted for suggesting that this was not the case; the idea that the heavy ponderous earth was rotating and moving in space around the sun seemed preposterous and contradicted all faith and common sense. The egocentric idea was so firmly embedded in men's minds that even after the acceptance of the motion of the earth and the planets around the sun, it was still believed that this solar system was in the centre of the universe of fixed stars. I was brought up on the idea that the sun was in the centre of a stellar system of many millions of stars distributed throughout such a volume of space that light would take 20,000 years to traverse the universe. Indeed, it was already too large for normal comprehension, and we seemed to be in a highly privileged position in the central regions of this great creation.

Today we realize that these conceptions give us altogether too parsimonious a view of the universe, and a quite inflated idea of the astronomical importance of our abode in space. In fact, we live on one of the smaller planets of a typical star. Our solar system is minute by cosmic standards. The most distant planet is only a few thousand million miles away, and the light from the sun reaches it in a few hours. The earth is moving very fast through space. The daily rotation is superimposed on its motion around the sun of 20 miles per second, and the entire system, sun, earth, planets, is rushing through interstellar space in the direction of a distant star cluster at the rate of over twelve miles a second. But this motion causes us no anxiety, interstellar space is very empty, the minute grains of interstellar dust which we encounter are insignificant compared with the bombardment which we suffer from the debris of our own system, and the nearest star is so far away that light from it travelling at 186,000 miles per second takes four years to reach us. Even if we were moving straight at this star we should take 60,000 years to get there.

Not only are we cosmically small, we are in a rather undignified position amongst the stars of the Milky Way. Our telescopes of the twentieth century have shown that the Milky Way contains about ten thousand million stars. These are not distributed uniformly, but exist in a flattened disk across which light takes about a hundred thousand years to travel. This vast system is itself turning around in space at the rate of once in a few hundred million years. The hub of this system, which we call the galactic centre, is a region of great interest, but unfortunately our view of it is very poor. We exist somewhere near the edge of this huge disk, and the central regions are obscured from view by clouds of interstellar dust. This dust obscures the view from the telescopes, and shuts out the light of the stars. We think that well over 90 per cent. of the starlight is obscured by the dust, otherwise the starlight would be as bright as a full moon. It is characteristic of man's skill that we have, today, at least partially restored our ego by devising means to penetrate this dust, and with our radio telescopes we can study the turmoil which is being enacted in the hub of the galaxy.

This Milky Way is itself only a local galactic system. The distances which separate the stars, the whole extent of the ten thousand million stars in the system, is as nothing compared with the separation of the galaxies in intergalactic space. If you look in the direction of the constellation Andromeda you can see there a very faint hazy patch of light. Herschel saw this and many similar nebulous patches in his telescope 150 years ago, and he speculated that they might lie outside the confines of the Milky Way. However, it needed the twentieth-century telescopes of Mount Wilson in America to resolve these nebulae into stars and produce the final evidence that they were, indeed, outside the Milky Way, and at very large distances. The light which reaches our telescopes from the Andromeda nebula has been travelling through space for two million years. It comes from another stellar system similar in size and content to our own Milky Way. Wherever we look in space we see these nebulae and within the region of the cosmos which we study with our modern telescopes they are almost countless—certainly thousands of millions and probably billions—all stellar systems made up of thousands of millions of stars. The 200-inch optical telescope at Palomar Mountain has identified these galaxies out to enormous distances. At the farthest limit of penetration the light has been on its journey through space for a few thousand million years, and we believe that the radio telescopes have penetrated even farther.

Some years ago we thought that these galaxies were isolated units in space, but now we believe that the galaxies exist in great groups or clusters. In the same way that the earth and planets are bound to the sun and move as a unit through space, so on an inconceivably vaster scale we think that the galaxies are contained in clusters as connected physical systems. The local group contains the Milky Way system, the Andromeda nebula, and perhaps two dozen others. It is not very populated, compared, for example, with the Virgo cluster of galaxies, which contains at least a thousand visible galaxies, although occupying only about twice the space of the local group.

The galaxies within these groups are in random motion—as it turns out—with dramatic consequences for the radio astronomer. Superimposed on this random motion, the groups as an entirety are taking part in the awe-inspiring large-scale expansion of the universe. As we recede into space the rate of expansion always increases. One object of our daily study in the constellation, Cygnus, is receding at the rate of more than 10,000 miles a second. Before I get home tonight its distance from us will have increased by more than the 93,-000,000 miles which separate the earth from the sun.

Today we argue amongst ourselves about the evolutionary processes, about the details of formation of stars and galaxies, about the interpretation of new observations, but the overall picture which I have given is not seriously questioned. In the three centuries since Galileo and Newton we have moved very far, but the vital break with tradition belongs to their age, not ours. Their victory is epitomized in the story of the evolution of man's ideas about the solar system—our battle in the dilemmas raised by the new instruments of astronomical research.

Today we accept without question the basic fact that the earth and the planets revolve around the sun in orbits described by Kepler's laws and by Newtonian theory, at least to a close approximation, but the stages by which man came to accept these simple mechanistic facts were painful and protracted. The story is mainly one of persecution of the astronomers on religious grounds, and therefore I want to say at the outset that this part of my talk is not to be construed as an attack on the religious organizations involved. In fact, if my theme were the interaction of organized religion on other human organizations during this period, then a recurrent trouble would be the attempts of the astronomers to upset the unitary conception of the cosmos, attempts which seemed to undermine the existing ethical and moral basis of life. I cannot enter into the discussion of the meaning of truth in this respect, but you will appreciate that my own life determines a particular outlook and that any attempt to suppress a scientific discovery I must regard as an attempt to suppress the truth. Even so, I cannot avoid considerable sympathy with some of the persecutors of the astronomers during this long struggle, although deploring their methods. For example, in the case of Bruno, who was burnt at the stake in 1600, his teaching was iconoclastic, and it would, I think, be easy for a moralist to justify the suppression of his work. I find myself with far less sympathy for the present-day attempts to suppress the results of certain astronomical investigations. There the roles are strangely reversed in a way which I will describe later when we consider the modern attempts to explain the origin of the solar system.

The popular idea that the struggle was primarily an affair involving Galileo in the early part of the seventeenth century is, I think, quite erroneous. Indeed, he represents the climax, and at his death the whole fabric of Aristotelian dynamics and astronomy lay in ruins. The religious doctrines were sensitive at two particular points. There was nearly always a violent reaction at any suggestion either that the earth might not be fixed at the centre of the system of stars and planets, or that the universe of stars was other than finite in time and space. Provided these basic tenets were not attacked, then the new ideas were often accommodated in religious teaching. The gradual absorption of Aristotle's ideas is a classic example. He taught that the stars and planets moved with uniform circular velocity in crystalline spheres, centred around the earth, and that the universe was limited in space. Today it may seem peculiar that such erroneous ideas could be retained for nearly two thousand years, and it is often stated that Aristotle obstructed the progress of astronomy. I think, however, that the stronghold lay not so much in the astronomical doctrine as such, but in the steady absorption of the doctrine with the current religious views. In any case the truth about the fundamental constitution of the solar system was vigorously suppressed whenever it began to emerge. Neither Aristarchus of Samos, who maintained that the earth and the planets revolved around the sun, nor Hipparchus and Ptolemy with their fine astronomical accomplishments managed to erase the conception of an earth fixed at the centre of the universe, although they discovered such relatively abstract phenomena as the precession of the equinoxes, and were able to predict with reasonable accuracy eclipses of the sun and moon.

The subsequent thousand years was a sombre period for astronomy. The Roman interest was limited to practical matters, such as the organization of the calendar, and there was a long period of stagnation in the development of man's ideas about the heavens. With the foundation of the universities and of the religious orders in the twelfth and thirteenth centuries a new interest arose in the study of the cosmos. Aristotle's writings were recovered, and the interpretation and adjustment of his astronomical ideas by St. Thomas Aquinas provided a coherent and acceptable framework for the development of medieval astronomy with ecclesiastical compatibility. Astrology was a predominant interest. The concept of the perfection of the circle as a geometrical figure was the basis for the belief that the fixed stars with their regular movements controlled the orderly events of the world. The more erratic movements of the planets were then held to be responsible for the vicissitudes of life, and the special relations of the Zodiacal signs, planets, and other heavenly bodies the precursors of disease and calamity. After the Turkish capture of Constantinople in the fifteenth century Pope Calixtus prayed: 'From the Turk and the comet, good Lord, deliver us!' Although today we look on such astrological doctrines with amused contempt, it is salutary to be reminded of their enormous strength by their survival to our own age in certain forms. For example, the occurrence of the great shower of Leonid meteors in the nineteenth century caused immense and widespread terror in the belief that the end of the world was at hand, and the appearance of a comet may still be endowed with a special significance.

The coherence established under the guidance of Aquinas between the ecclesiastical doctrines and the basic idea of the fixed earth and finite universe, provided an organized scheme of great strength which formed the basis for physical and theological teaching in the Middle Ages. Attempts to undermine the central features of this scheme were bound to lead to bitter struggles, and, indeed, forces other than the development of new theoretical ideas were necessary before man could make progress in astronomy. In the fifteenth century the belief that theoretical ideas could be adjusted by experimental observations began to grow, and with the sixteenth century we reach the age of the decisive intellectual battles, a century which holds the lives of Copernicus, Tycho Brahe, Kepler, and Galileo. Vast changes were introduced in man's ideas of the universe in the name of Copernicus. Although his scheme retained much of current theory—such as that the universe was finite, terminating in the sphere of the fixed stars—his explanation of the movement of bodies in the solar system was basically correct in so far that he imbued the earth and the planets with motion around the sun.

A casual reading of history does not give the impression that Copernicus suffered the agony of persecution of his predecessors and successors. He escaped the severe penalties which were later to fall on Bruno and Galileo. But there should be no illusions about the temper of those times. About Copernicus, Luther said, 'The fool will turn the whole science of astronomy upside down. But, as Holy Writ declares, it was the sun and not the earth which Joshua commanded to stand still.' The ferment of the Reformation weakened the coherence of the antagonists, and the Catholic denunciation of the Copernican theory was delayed for many years. Copernicus was aware of the dangers which surrounded him and most cleverly attempted to place himself under Papal protection by dedicating his work to Pope Paul III. Amongst many reasons which he gave for claiming the Pope's protection was that his work would help to solve the problem of calendar reform about which he had been consulted by Rome in 1514. Indeed, in this Copernicus was justified, since many years later Pope Gregory used the Copernican tables in his reform of the calendar.

The full significance of Copernicus's *De Revolutionibus* was apparent only to the mathematicians and astronomers who could understand it. The dissemination of the Copernican theory in philosophic form did not occur for another forty years. Then a renegade friar from Naples, Giordano Bruno, came to London and in 1584 published three small works based on the ideas of Nicolas of Cusa, and on the astronomical scheme of Copernicus. Whereas the Copernican system retained the Aristotelian idea of the finite universe of fixed stars, Bruno also taught that the universe was infinite in time and space. As far as the Christianity of his day was concerned these ideas were pagan in the extreme, since the very idea of creation was attacked. Now the suppressed rage of the Church was turned on Bruno, and after some years in the prisons of the Inquisition he was burned at the stake in 1600.

With this hideous event we enter the final period of bitter persecution with which the name of Galileo is inseparably linked. In the history of astronomy Galileo is uniquely distinguished because in 1609 he first used a telescope to study the heavens. However, before that period of his life opened he had delivered further mortal blows at the Aristotelian scheme by his work on falling bodies and by his observation of a stellar nova, or new star, in the outer region of the fixed stars which should be the perfect unchanging region. With the telescope he observed the lunar mountains and discovered the spots on the sun, thereby destroying the belief that the heavenly bodies were perfect spheres without blemish. He observed the phases of Venus and discovered the moons of Jupiter. This observational evidence in support of the basic mathematical scheme of Copernicus and the more refined system of Kepler marked the final ruin of the Aristotelian scheme.

Kepler was a Protestant, a mystic and a dreamer, who produced volumes of obscure mathematics out of which emerged his famous laws of planetary motion. He was persecuted by the Protestant faculty of his university and was driven to take refuge with the Jesuits. Galileo was an intellectual giant, with brilliant social gifts, and a most devout member of the Roman Church. He was too much aware of the grievous issues at hand to pursue his astronomical observations in isolation from the articles which governed the fundamental edicts of the Church. In 1615 he voluntarily came to Rome in order to seek a modification of current teaching. Through a tangled vein of personal intrigue and animosities in which Cardinal Bellarmine rather than Pope Paul V was chiefly involved, the Qualifiers of the Holy Office were summoned to give their opinion on two propositions. First, that the sun is the centre of the world, and hence immovable of local motion, second, the earth is not the centre of the world, nor immovable, but moves according to the whole of itself, also with a diurnal motion. The Qualifiers declared the first proposition to be 'foolish and absurd, philosophically and formally heretical, inasmuch as it expressly contradicts the doctrine of the Holy Scripture in many passages, both in their literal meaning and according to the general interpretation of the Fathers and Doctors' and the second was declared 'to receive the same censure in philosophy and, as regards theological truth, to be at least erroneous in faith.'

The injunction was transmitted to Galileo by Bellarmine in private audience. Galileo believed that Bellarmine had commanded 'that he must neither hold nor defend that opinion'. Sixteen years later at the second and greater crisis of his life he was informed that the command was 'not to hold, defend, nor teach that opinion in any way whatsoever'. Contemporary research still leaves us uncertain whether Galileo was deceived by Bellarmine or the Pope, or whether false documents were lodged in the file.

Seven years later Paul V was succeeded by Urban VIII, an enlightened man who eagerly sought the presence of Galileo. Indeed, Galileo wrote at this time 'I am revolving in my mind plans of some moment for the republic of letters, and perhaps can never hope for so wonderful a combination of circumstances to ensure their success'. With the encouragement of the Pope Galileo published his fateful *Dialogue* in 1632, which was greeted with rapturous praise. Alas, within a year he was on trial before the Inquisition. The reason for this reversal of fortune are somewhat obscure. The Jesuits were responsible, at least for the initial moves. For many years Galileo had been engaged in a subsidiary, but bitter dispute with a Jesuit astronomer—Father Scheiner—about the discovery and meaning of sunspots. Urban VIII was distracted by political troubles, and the trial is rent with jealousies and animosities which often obscure the main issues. The Inquisitors were themselves in a predicament as to whether to base their charge on the Injunction of 1616, or on the contents of the *Dialogue*. Their sentence was neither unanimous, nor harsh by modern standards, and Galileo lived the remaining years of his life under house arrest on his farm near Arcetri.

It is the fashion to blame the Roman Church for this persecution of Galileo; it is indeed convenient to blame the Church, or Urban VIII or the thirteen Cardinals of the Inquisition. I think, however, that we should do well to remember, first, that Galileo was led by his brilliant intuitive gifts to do battle with a persistence which may have been somewhat intemperate, and secondly, that his persecutors appear to have been the victims of a muddle and intrigue quite out of keeping with the great philosophical and religious system which they were intended to guard.

Galileo attacked the entire foundations of Aristotle's science on a broad front; he produced evidence, as distinct from ideas. However, he was too close in time to Kepler and too far from Newton to produce the vital connecting link between the Earth and the Cosmos. He left a great breach in the thousand-year-old philosophical scheme without any immediately replacement, yet he sought the abandonment of the whole. At this distance in time we can, I think, appreciate the dilemma of the Cardinals.

The death of Galileo coincided with the birth of the man who was to provide the vital links in the Galilean cosmos. The half century which elapsed between the appearance of Galileo's *Dialogues* and Newton's *Principia* was a period in which reason still revolted against the movement of the earth. The yearning for the old conceptions lingered. The meeting of Milton and Galileo inspired the poet, but the cosmology of *Paradise Lost* belongs to Ptolemy, not to Copernicus and Galileo:

> *how build, unbuild, contrive*
> *To save appearances, how gird the sphere*
> *with Centric and Eccentric scribbled o'er,*
> *Cycle and Epicycle, Orb in Orb . . .*

The Archangel Raphael tells Adam that *whether Heaven move or Earth . . .*

> *From Man or Angel the great Architect*
> *Did wisely to conceal, and not divulge*
> *His secrets to be scanned by them who ought*
> *Rather admire . . .*

However, this particular battle was rapidly moving into the intellectual sphere. At the time of the publication of *Paradise Lost* The Royal Society was already in existence, and Newton had conceived his *Principia*. The opponents of the Copernican school had reason as well as faith on their side. In postulating the movement of the earth around the sun, neither Copernicus, Kepler, nor Galileo had succeeded in explaining two enormous difficulties. The first was the dynamical problem of the maintenance of the diurnal and annual movement of the earth, and the second was the gravitational problem. The teaching was that heavy objects aspired to reach the centre of the earth because it was the centre of the universe. In the Arisotelian scheme the planets were maintained in their crystalline spheres and thereby prevented from falling. By removing the earth from its central position, the astronomers raised this subsidiary dilemma, that if the earth was no longer the centre of the universe why should heavy objects still aspire to fall towards the centre of the earth? The distraction which followed in the wake of

Galileo throws into relief the greatness of Newton. His enunciation of the law of universal gravitation, that the force between two bodies is proportional to their masses and varies inversely as the square of their distance apart, provided the synthesis which linked the falling apple with the rotation of the planets and the integration of Kepler's laws of planetary motion with the observations of Galileo. Newton rationalized the universe, at least as it was observable at that time. He introduced a determinism in man's ideas of the workings of the universe, which marked the final downfall of the ancient cosmologies and of their associated theologies. Men's minds were freed and the conflict moved to new fields.

II. The Origin of the Solar System

I DO NOT think that since the time of Newton it has ever been seriously contended that the solar system is an accidental aggregation of bodies in space. By terrestrial standards the distances separating the sun, earth, and planets are very large. We are about ninety-three million miles from the sun, and the distant planet Pluto is over three and a half thousand million miles away. On the other hand, the nearest star is over twenty billion miles distant. To bring these dimensions down to more manageable quantities, one can say that light from the sun takes 8 minutes on its way to the earth, over 5 hours to the planet Pluto, but 4 years to the nearest star. By the standards of the cosmos, the solar system is therefore an extremely compact unit. Moreover, the planets and the earth move around the sun in orbits which are almost circular, and all these orbits lie nearly in the same plane. The sun is rotating in the same sense as the planets, and the entire system is moving as a unit through interstellar space with a speed of about forty-five thousand miles per hour. It is therefore only reasonable to proceed on the assumption that the bodies of the solar system shared a common origin and have evolved to their present condition by orderly processes. Over one hundred and fifty years have now elapsed since Laplace made the first attempt in scientific form to explain the origin of the system. However, objections have been found to every suggestion made, and I believe it would be correct to say that there are more theories of the origin of the solar system than there are of the entire universe.

In the stream of astronomical and mathematical work poured out by Laplace from Paris in the late eighteenth and early nineteenth centuries was his famous nebular hypothesis of the origin of the solar system. To a certain extent the idea had been anticipated in more general philosophical form by Swedenborg and Kant, but the scientific plausibility of the theory is entirely due to Laplace. He believed that at some remote epoch all the material which now forms the sun and the solar system was a vast nebula of rarefied gas, in slow rotation. This nebula cooled slowly, and as it did so the gas contracted because of the internal gravitational forces. The rotation quickened as the contraction continued. Eventually the rotation became so rapid that some of the gas became detached from the periphery and formed a ring outside the nebula. This happened repeatedly, with the rotation of the remaining nebula always increasing. Finally, the remaining central portion of the nebula condensed into the sun and the material in each ring collected into the separate planets. This theory of Laplace accounted for many of the observed features of the solar system— such as the orbits of the planets around the sun in nearly the same plane—and it enjoyed a long period of success and popularity. Eventually two fatal objections were raised. Clerk Maxwell proved that the rings of material successively detached from the periphery of the shrinking nebula would never coalesce into single large planets, but in course of time would be transformed into a collection of much smaller bodies—like Saturn's rings, for example. The second objection, which has been the downfall of many later theories, is concerned with the momentum of the planetary system. Now, momentum is our measurement of the quantity of motion of a moving body. A large mass obviously has more momentum (that is, a larger quantity of motion) than a smaller one moving at the same speed. In fact, we calculate momentum by multiplying mass by velocity. Because the planets are moving in orbit around the sun, and not in a straight line, we call their momentum rotational momentum. Now the masses and velocities of all the planets in the solar system are known. As you might expect, the sun is far heavier than all the planets put together. It weighs a thousand million trillion tons, whereas the earth and planets weigh only a million trillion tons. In fact, 99.9 per cent. of the mass of the solar system is concentrated in the sun. If we multiply these masses by the velocities of the planets to get the momenta, it would be natural to expect that nearly all the rotational momentum would be carried by the sun. On the contrary, we find the opposite to be the case. In fact, 98 per cent. of the momentum is concentrated in the planets. Now this is a most unexpected result. It arises because the planets are moving very fast in their orbits compared with the rate of rotation of the sun. This segregation of mass and velocity must have occurred long ago, when the peripheral rings separated from the main nebula. If 98 per cent. of the momenta was concentrated in these rings, which represented such a negligible part of the entire mass, then the velocities must have been enormous, and condensation, even into small asteroids, would have been impossible.

The nebular hypothesis was subject to this searching criticism in the second part of the nineteenth century, and the longest lived and most famous of the solar-system theories had to be abandoned, although indeed, as we shall see, some of its basic conceptions reappear in current theories. At the turn of the century two American astronomers, Chamberlin and Moulton, suggested another type of origin for the solar system in an attempt to overcome the basic troubles of the nebular theory. Their hypothesis was that in the remote past our sun was an ordinary star without planets. Then, about twenty million years ago, another star in its journey through space passed very close to the sun. The gravitational attraction between the two bodies swung them about one another and eventually the other star passed on. But in this close encounter great tides of gaseous matter would have been torn from the sun; some of this would fall back, some might have followed the passing star into space, but a certain amount would remain under the gravitational field of the sun, circling around it. These gases eventually condensed into small fragments, which finally accreted into larger and larger bodies to form the planets. The idea that the primeval material of the earth and planets arose from an encounter between two stars in this way has been the forerunner of many succeeding theories. Perhaps the most famous of these was popularized by Jeans thirty years ago. This was the tidal theory of Jeans and Jeffreys, according to which the star which approached the sun pulled out a great filament of gas, which broke up and condensed into the planets straight away, without any intermediate accretion process as in the earlier theory. The validity of these theories was undermined by the American astronomer, H. N. Russell, in 1935, who showed that in any such encounter the approaching star would have to come so close to the sun that the planets would eventually move in orbits many thousands of times closer to their parent than are actually observed.

I do not intend to follow through the many variations of detail which have since been suggested in order to make these encounter theories more acceptable, but I am anxious to explain the position as it has developed during the last few years. In this connexion the growth of interest in the problem of the origin of the solar system by astronomers in Russia is a feature of particular interest. My account of the developments during the last 150 years has so far been singularly free from those entanglements with doctrine which submerged the evolution of astronomical ideas until the seventeenth century. Now we begin to find a very strange situation. In the printed Russian books dealing with this problem we find that the study is justified because of its importance in the elaboration of a correct materialist world outlook. The distinguished Russian astronomer, Otto Schmidt, said this about Jeans's theory of the origin of the solar system: '. . . What, in the astronomer's view, was the shortcoming of the Jeans hypothesis—that is, the extreme rarity of the planetary formation process—became its chief merit in the eyes of the layman who did not want to break with religion. Jeans's hypothesis was a most acceptable compromise. The rarity of planetary formation in Jeans's scheme is, of course, still not idealism in itself—there are rare phenomena in Nature—but it opened the gates to idealism in cosmogony. . . .' A recent scientific paper by another eminent Russian astronomer says this: 'The development of cosmogony in the capitalist countries is hampered by the idealistic world outlook that prevails there. Some Western astronomers directly repair to religion. However, the pursuit of natural science impels scientists to take the materialist path. And so we find scientists who correctly approach the study of the origin and evolution of heavenly bodies, and obtain valuable results.'

Later on I shall speak with the very warmest approval of the scientific developments in the U.S.S.R., but here one begins to see another less happy side of progress in that country. Now the wheel has turned full circle. The delicate equilibrium which has existed for the last two hundred years is once more in danger. For two thousand years the compatibility of astronomical theory with religious doctrine was a prerequisite for its acceptance and indeed for the safety of its originator. Now in the materialist world view such compatibility is a reason for complaint; a philosophy has once more become part of scientific method. 'Cosmogony in the U.S.S.R.', we are told, 'is based on the firm materialist traditions of Russian science.' You must remember that in so far as relations with Russian colleagues are concerned I move in a restricted circle. Within that circle I see provision for astronomical research on a scale which is likely to exceed anything else in the world during the next ten years. At the same time this is accompanied by this subtle intellectual hindrance, which if it develops, may well prejudice the great astronomical developments which are taking place in that country. For example, although today Russia has at least as many astronomers as any other country, there is a peculiar gap in that there is no school concerned with the ultimate cosmological problem of the expansion and origin of the universe. This vast and intractable problem which I shall talk about in my last lectures has, at present, no obvious solution in terms of established scientific concepts. The belief that the political philosophy restrains Russian astronomers from working in this subject is strengthened by the ban which exists on the translation of books dealing with the evolution and expansion of the universe. I suspect, however, that these hindrances may be a transitional phase because the attempt to suppress will be defeated by the very efficiency and thoroughness of the educational system. Indeed, the ban which I have given as an example is already undermined by the comprehensive collection of the original English and American works on cosmology in the libraries of those Russian astronomers who have contact with the West. Whatever dispute there may be over these views, one thing remains beyond contention. It is that we have entered an epoch where Russian astronomy can compete with the best which the world can offer. Contemporary Russian work on the problem of the solar system is an indication of the rapid postwar resurrection of astronomy in the U.S.S.R. When the encounter theories of the origin of the solar system had to be abandoned new ideas began to emerge, and in these developments Otto Schmidt and the astronomers at his Institute in Moscow have played a prominent part. In its basic form the idea marks a partial return to the nebular hypothesis of Kant and Laplace, in the suggestion that the planets originated from a diffuse cloud of material surrounding the sun. Laplace suggested that the planets condensed from this gaseous material, but in the new theory the cloud consists of a mixture of dust and gas, and the planets are formed through a gradual accretion of these cold particles. As this huge primordial cloud rotated around the sun the dust particles gradually concentrated into a flattened disk. Innumerable collisions occurred between the primeval dust particles, at each collision the relative velocities of the colliding particles decreasing, the energy being radiated away as heat, until appreciable aggregates, or embryos, began to form in this cloud. These embryos marked the transition of the dust into solid bodies, perhaps with diameters of 100 miles. At this stage in prehistory the turmoil in the dust cloud became tremendous, because these embryos began to collide with one another, and in doing so must have been shattered into fragments. But all the time the accretion process was going on, and the cloud soon began to form into a multitude of solid bodies of different sizes and mass, with the embryos which escaped destruction growing faster and faster and eventually forming the major planets. The earth would not have grown directly from an accumulation of the primeval dust, but by a process of disintegration of the colliding embryos and successive accumulations of the fragments with the dust particles. A few thousand million years would be required for these processes to mature. The bombardment of the earth with the dust is still going on at the rate of millions of tons per year—but we have to launch an earth satellite before finding it, because the dust is now stopped by our protective atmosphere. Apart from the occasional meteorites which plunge through the atmosphere, we have reached a peaceful stage in the evolution of the dust cloud.

Indeed, the meteorites which reach the earth provide our only direct access to extra-terrestrial material. They are believed to come from the region of the asteroids. That is to say, the wide gap in the sequence of planetary orbits between Mars and Jupiter. In this region there are many thousands of minor planets or asteroids. It has been popularly supposed that these are the remnants of a planet which once existed between Mars and Jupiter and which exploded at some time in the past. However, it seems more likely that the asteroids are the embryonic accretions which failed to grow into a planet of appreciable size. Only a few of these are as much as a hundred miles in diameter, but the numbers increase rapidly as the size diminishes, and there is no obvious distinction between the small asteroids of the size of a mountain and the great meteorite weighing hundreds of tons which crashed into Siberia in 1908. The analysis of the structure of these meteorites leaves little doubt that they have passed through the successive stages of accretion and fragmentation.

The accretion theory overcomes the major trouble of the older ideas. I think it would be correct to say that most of the astronomers who study the problem today would accept the basic idea of the evolution from a cloud of dust and gas, although there are many variations possible in the stages of formation of the earth and planets from this primeval material. The rapid accumulation of new data about the solar system, and particularly the possibility that earth satellites will shortly give us a more intimate acquaintance with the nearer planets, will soon narrow the possible range of theoretical speculations about the origin of our immediate environment in space. It is, I think, likely that these modern variations of the Kant–Laplace theories will now gradually come together into an agreed scheme which can satisfactorily explain the known features of the present state of the solar system. There is, however, a profound question which remains unanswered. It is this. I have discussed the accretion

theory in terms of the evolution of a cloud of dust and
gas over the past few thousand million years. If we
probe still farther back in time, what do we find? Where
did this cloud come from? In particular, did it form as
part of the original sun, or was it acquired by the sun
long after its own formation? The embryos in the dust
cloud must have begun to form in an epoch between
about three thousand million and six thousand million
years ago. Now, as we shall see later, the stars and
galaxies are much older—perhaps nine thousand million years old. I am now asking you to think of this
intervening period, because before we can be satisfied
about the origin of the solar system we must decide
what happened in this remote epoch.

You might think that this is a highly academic question, but I cannot take that view, because on our answer
may well rest the issue of the uniqueness of the planetary system and hence of life as it is known on earth.
Our views about such a question cut at the very basis
of existence. During the formative years of my own life,
I was never troubled by this. I was taught, on the one
hand, that we were unique, and on the other hand,
that our local system was torn out of the sun according
to the tidal theory of Jeans. There was no conflict, because the passage of another star close enough to the
sun to cause such an eruption was a very rare occurrence. Although the sun was merely one of a hundred
thousand million stars in the local galaxy, and many

millions of similar galaxies existed, the mathematicians could show that the approach of any two of these stars close enough to erupt the tides required by the theory would be, indeed, very rare. The uniqueness of the planetary system and of ourselves was therefore not in question. But now we have moved into a new age the ideas of accidental encounters have had to be abandoned, and the whole question of the multiplicity of planetary systems in the universe is again wide open.

The problem before us is one of immense difficulty. In fact, my own view is that in some ways the problem is greater than that of the origin of the whole universe. In the case of the universe we now have instruments which can penetrate into regions of space where we obtain knowledge of the state of things as they were thousands of millions of years ago—that is, we can still study regions which may represent the early evolutionary stages of the cosmos. But in the case of our solar system this is impossible. The conversion of the cloud into planets has almost entirely effaced the traces of its own genesis, and we are prevented from making any observations to test the theories of the origin of the cloud.

In fact, there do not seem to be many possibilities which would satisfy all the subsequent criteria. The ideas fall into two groups: either the dust cloud was captured by the sun, at a time when the sun was already well advanced in its own evolution as an ordinary star, or the sun and the cloud were born at the same time.

Otto Schmidt and the Russian school believed in the first idea, that the sun captured the cloud when it passed through a dense region of interstellar dust. A few years ago Hoyle also believed in the capture theory, but in a quite different form. He suggested that the sun was once a member of a binary star system. These double-star systems in which two stars revolve around one another are quite common, and Hoyle's idea was that the binary companion of the sun exploded with extreme violence—in fact, that it was a case of a supernova. The violence of the disintegration would be such that the remains of the star would be blown far away from the sun except for a small amount of the dust and gas which was captured to form the primeval solar nebula.

Nowadays Hoyle believes that the sun was born as one member of an entire cluster of stars and that in the beginning the sun and the cloud were one vast nebula of the type pictured by Laplace. I should perhaps mention here that it is no longer considered likely that individual stars condense from the primeval interstellar gas; analysis shows that it is more probable that the huge clouds of interstellar gas condense into hundreds or even thousands of stars simultaneously. Incidentally, these modern ideas of stellar associations owe much to the work of the Russian astronomer, Ambartzumian. In postulating that the solar nebula is

simply a phase in the normal processes of star formation, a serious difficulty arises. The common elements
which make up the earth and the planets are believed
to have been formed from the primeval hydrogen gas
by the thermonuclear processes which can take place
only in the hot and dense conditions in the nucleus of
a star or the sun. But in the theory of the formation
of the solar system which we are now discussing, the
separation of the planetary cloud from the shrinking
nebula must occur before the central regions get hot
enough for these thermonuclear processes to begin. We
still have to explain how the earth and many of the
planets consist of elements which could not be produced from the primeval gas of the solar nebula unless
it was subject to this intense heat and pressure of a
stellar interior. Hoyle's explanation is that among the
cloud of stars in which the sun was born, one or more
of them were supernovae, and the explosion scattered
the elements which had already been formed in their
interiors amongst the condensing nebulae of the other
stars. Thus the hydrogen gas of the solar nebula would
become mixed with the material necessary for the building of the earth and planets.

Although astronomers now tend to agree about the
formation of the earth and the planets from the original
nebula by accretion, our ideas about the events which
led to the genesis of the primeval cloud a few thousand
million years ago are, at present, very uncertain and are

likely to remain so for a long time.

On the other hand, the possibilities now offered for the genesis of the cloud have a common feature. It is very unlikely to have been a rare event in the cosmos. In fact, modern cosmogony can accept a situation in which most of the stars in the Milky Way have planetary systems similar to our own. Even if we put in tremendous odds of one in a million against a similar subsequent planetary evolution the numbers remain staggering. We would still have a hundred thousand similar systems in the Milky Way, and over a billion in the regions of the universe which we can now reach with our telescopes. The question of the evolution of some forms of living material elsewhere in the universe is therefore removed from the astronomical to the biological domain. There I cannot proceed, although in this connexion it must be remembered that the new ideas about the origin of the solar system have other important consequences apart from the multiplicity of similar systems. According to the old theories the earth was formed in a molten state, and the existence of even the most primitive form of organic material would have been impossible until the outer layers had cooled. In this case the evolution of organic material could only have begun at a rather late stage in the history of the earth. Although there is still much argument about the detailed processes, the current evidence is overwhelming that the earth and the planets were not formed in a molten state, but by the accretion of cold solid bodies. The high temperatures which exist in the deep interior arose later because of the tremendous pressures which developed and from the processes of radioactive heating. In the final stages of accretion the outer layers remained cool, and if any complex molecules or organisms already existed in the dust cloud they retained their identity.

The question of the existence of some form of life elsewhere in the solar system has long been the subject of speculation. We are at present moving headlong towards a final resolution of the problem. The flight of the American lunar probe, Pioneer, was a clear demonstration that man has already achieved sufficient technical ability to send his instruments into the vicinity of the moon and the nearer planets. Direct contact between some form of space probe and the moon, and at least the direct sampling of some planetary atmospheres, must be close at hand. We are today faced with opportunities which were inconceivable a few years ago. The basic problem in the origin of life concerns the formation and duplication of complex molecules. The sampling of the moon dust, and the planetary atmospheres and surfaces might give vital information on the possible existence of these pre-life processes in the primeval material of the solar system. These opportunities carry with them the most appalling dangers. If the probing is carried out recklessly, or with insufficient skill or preparation, then the extra-terrestrial bodies will be contaminated with the macromolecules which have developed on earth. The solution of the problem of extra-terrestrial life would then be for ever in jeopardy, and man might unwittingly assume the responsibility of prejudicing the development of organisms elsewhere in the solar system.

Whatever the future holds in respect of the solar system investigations, we would do well to accustom ourselves to the implications of the multiplicity of planetary systems in the Universe. I cannot help but observe that the biologist must introduce inconceivable changes against evolution elsewhere if we are to preserve our uniqueness. I think of Kant, who in another age and by other reasoning reached similar conclusions but resisted this implication: 'Oh! happy will be the soul,' he said, 'if, amid the tumult of the elements and the dreams of nature, she is always elevated to a height from whence she can see the devastations which their own perishableness brings upon the things of the world as they thunder past beneath her feet.'

III. The New Astronomy

For over three hundred years after Galileo first looked at the sky through a small telescope, man's progress in astronomy was closely associated with the construction of larger and larger telescopes. The primary stimulus came from Herschel in the late eighteenth century. He began to make his own telescopes in 1773 when he was an organist in Bath. In the following ten years he is believed to have made over 500 telescope mirrors of various sizes. He caused a sensation by discovering the planet Uranus, the first planet discovered since prehistoric times, but his main interest was in the arrangement of the stars in the heavens.

In a paper which he read to the Royal Society in 1785 on the 'Construction of the Heavens', Herschel explained why he found it necessary to build larger telescopes. To the unaided eye the Milky Way appears as a diffuse band of light across the sky. Through a small telescope it is seen to be a collection of stars, but many nebulous patches remain unresolved. Herschel said that as the power of the telescope is increased an observer 'perceives that those objects which had been called nebulae are evidently nothing but clusters of stars. He finds their number increase upon him, and when he resolves one nebula into stars he discovers ten new ones which he cannot resolve.'

In those words Herschel described his own experience and expressed the challenge which still faces astronomers today. The succession of telescopes of ever-increasing size which have since been constructed has continued to reveal more and more distant nebulae of stars. However, it seems likely that we have nearly reached the culmination of this line of development with the 200-inch telescope on Palomar Mountain in America which began its programme of work about 15 years ago. Culmination, because it seems possible that optical telescopes of this order of size may represent the largest which it is worth while building on earth. Even under the excellent atmospheric conditions which exist on Palomar, the unsteadiness of the atmosphere limits the realization of the maximum penetration of this telescope to a few dozen nights during the year.

This telescope can photograph star systems which are so far away that the light has taken over two thousand million years to reach us, but when I discuss the problem of the origin of the universe you will realize that this distance is a most tantalizing limit. The desire to find out what lies beyond is very great—some knowledge of the star systems at twice this distance might well give us the key to unlock the secrets of the evolution of the entire universe. You will therefore understand that those of us who seek this knowledge seize with a particular passion any prospects of surmounting the hindrances of our earthbound environment. And indeed we have been born in a fortunate and exciting epoch. Out of the cataclysm of a world war have emerged two technical developments which are creating a revolution in astronomical observations—radio astronomy and the earth satellite.

When I think of the enormous scientific and technological problems which had to be solved I still stand in awe when I reflect that at this moment[1] at least four objects launched by man are relentlessly circling this earth. They have carried scientific instruments above the dense regions of the earth's atmosphere and are sending back by radio the information about the conditions in the environment of the earth which hitherto we have only been able to probe remotely and by inference. The astronomer whose interest lies in the problems of the solar system has already gathered a rich harvest of results about the complex of radiations and particles which exist in space and which are normally absorbed or transformed by processes in the

---

[1] *The moment in question was at the time of the original broadcast on 23 November, 1958, when the Vanguard satellite, Explorer IV, Sputnik 3, and its carrier rocket were all in orbit.*

upper regions of the atmosphere. Soon, telescopes will be carried into these regions and man's vision will be freed from the disturbing effects of the atmosphere. Limitless possibilities are now emerging; indeed, we seem to be on the verge of another epoch of discovery which may well parallel that of the radio telescope.

In the ordinary course of events our knowledge of the universe comes to us because the sun and the stars emit light. Less than 30 years ago Jansky, an American engineer, discovered almost by accident that radio waves were reaching the earth from outer space. But although his proof that they were coming from regions of space outside the solar system was quite decisive, he could not find out much more about these radio waves. Radio waves and light waves travel through space with the same speed, 186,000 miles a second, but are distinguished by the difference in wavelength. The light which reaches us from the stars has a wavelength measurable in millionths of a centimetre whereas the wavelength of the radio waves is measured in metres. To detect these radio waves we need a special kind of telescope, now commonly known as a radio telescope, which is in effect, a very large version of the common television aerial. The urge to build big radio telescopes is the same as the driving force behind the construction of large optical telescopes, namely, the desire to penetrate far into space. Because of the long wavelength of the radio waves the radio telescopes have to be very much larger than optical telescopes. Even with the enormous instruments now in operation the radio-astronomer's view of the heavens is ill-defined compared with that given by a small optical telescope. This factor greatly increases the difficulty of correlating the universe which we study with radio telescopes with the stars and galaxies visible to our eyes.

It is hardly surprising that Jansky and those who followed him were unable to relate their radio signals with the stellar objects perceived by our normal senses, and for a long time the idea existed that these radio waves were coming from the hydrogen gas which fills the space between the stars. For years Jansky's discovery remained almost unknown, and this unexpected gift of nature to man lay disregarded by the world's astronomers. My own introduction to this work was accidental—a casual remark by a colleague during the endless wartime discussions on how to get a few more miles of range out of our radar. Yet within four years I was wanting most desperately the telescope which now towers over the Cheshire plain. You see, the wartime developments in radar had placed in our hands equipment of a sensitivity and excellence far greater than anything previously available. As soon as these new techniques were used to study the radio waves from the sky one realized that Jansky's discovery had opened an entirely new avenue for the exploration of space.

The improved definition and sensitivity of the equipment soon showed that some of the radio emission was concentrated in particular parts of the sky. The idea that the interstellar hydrogen gas emitted the radio waves turned out to be only a small part of the story. The real situation was much more exciting. The concentration of the radio emissions into localized sources does not seem to occur in any regions of the heavens in which there are prominent visible objects. On the other hand, if we turn our radio telescopes towards the bright stars like Sirius or Capella we cannot record any radio waves from them. Indeed, we face a paradox which has sometimes made us reflect on those heavenly bodies of Lucretius 'which glide devoid of light forevermore'. However, we do not now believe that these newly discovered radio sources are dark stars. Our difficulty in relating them to the universe of our ordinary vision arises, we think, partly because the objects which emit radio waves are very faint and generally peculiar, and partly because the radio waves come from distant regions which are beyond the range of the optical telescopes.

Before I talk further about this situation it would, I think, be helpful if I described the results of our attempts to detect radio emissions from the more common stars and galaxies. To begin with, the sun is a very strong radio source—so strong indeed that it sometimes hinders the observations of the more distant signals, in the same way that its light blocks out stars from the ordinary telescopes. One of the earliest of the post-war surprises was the discovery by Appleton and Hey that the sun spots and flares which occasionally appear on the solar surface are associated with great and irregular increases in the solar radio emissions. These solar eruptions are often accompanied by disturbing terrestrial events such as the appearance of the aurora borealis and the fade-outs in transatlantic radio-communications. When the sun is quiet, or undisturbed by spots, then the radio waves from the sun are much less intense. They are generated in the solar corona, that highly tenuous region of the sun extending far outside the photosphere which is the disk of the sun which we see normally. For the radio astronomer the size of the sun depends on the wavelength which he uses to study it. At a radio wavelength of a few centimetres we find that the sun is about the same size as the sun which we see with our eyes, but as the wavelength we use increases so does the size of the sun as seen by the radio astronomer. At a few metres' wavelength its radius is several times greater than the optical radius. If our eyes were sensitive to these radio wavelengths the sun would appear to be enormous and probably flattened, not spherical as it now appears. The subjective basis for our knowledge of the sun introduces a nice point for philosophical argument.

Of the planets in our solar system, Jupiter at least

behaves abnormally as far as the radio astronomer is concerned. About four years ago scientists in Washington got some unexpected deflections on the chart connected to their radio telescope. For a long time they thought it was some local interference but after a few months the same kind of interference began to appear in the middle of the night and eventually they realized that the signals were coming from the planet Jupiter. Now these results are very surprising, since, unlike the sun, Jupiter does not have the kind of hot atmosphere conducive to the generation of radio waves. It now seems possible that these signals come from the planetary surface, and recent work has indicated that if this is the case only a few places on the surface are responsible. It is interesting to speculate on the events which might generate these signals, since the energies involved are enormous. In fact, it is difficult to establish a parallel with anything which might happen on earth. One has to think in terms of the energy of ten or more hydrogen bombs, or giant volcanic eruptions like the explosion of Krakatau. We may well have to wait for the close approach of a space probe to Jupiter before this problem can be settled.

After these remarks about the radio emissions from the sun and Jupiter you may be somewhat puzzled by my earlier reference to the difficulty of detecting radio waves from the common visible objects in the universe. The sun is a common star, and one might therefore expect other stars in the Milky Way to emit similar radio waves. Indeed, they might well do so, but even the nearest star is over 200,000 times farther from us than the sun. If the sun were at that distance its radio waves would be 50,000 million times more difficult to detect and that presents us with an almost insuperable problem. Actually if these distant stars also have occasional great outbursts, then the radio waves emitted on these occasions might just be detectable by a large instrument like the telescope at Jodrell Bank. Such a search is in progress, but whatever the result it is clear that any radio emissions of this kind from common stars do not make any significant contribution to the radio waves which are emanating from the regions of the Milky Way.

When we turn our radio telescopes in the direction of the Milky Way we are studying radio waves which have been on their journey for many thousands of years. As I said in my first lecture, the Milky Way is an assemblage of ten thousand million stars arranged in the form of a flattened disk across which light would take 100,000 years to travel. As for the radio waves from the Milky Way, the only conclusive statement which I would be prepared to make is that they certainly do not originate in these stars. The Milky Way as revealed to the radio telescopes is not such a flattened disk. It is surrounded by a halo, or corona, of radio emission. The existence of this corona was inferred a year or so ago by the Russian astronomer, Schlovsky, whose idea was confirmed by the measurements of the radio astronomers in Cambridge, and this summer two of my colleagues using the Jodrell Bank telescope have found evidence for similar haloes around the distant extragalactic nebulae; that is to say, nebulae outside the Milky Way. We do not yet know how to interpret these discoveries because there is nothing visible in the optical telescopes outside the main stellar structure of these nebulae. Hoyle and Gold are convinced that the radio waves in these regions are emanating from high-energy particles moving in extensive magnetic fields, and that these same particles are the source of the cosmic radiation. If this linkage can be substantiated a most important step will have been made in our understanding of some fundamental astrophysical processes.

When we consider the radio emissions which come from the regions of the Milky Way defined by the assemblage of stars, we find a complicated situation which is not yet fully understood. Two features are of particular interest. Between the stars it has for long been realized that there must exist great clouds of hydrogen gas, but this gas is in a neutral state and does not emit light and so cannot be seen with ordinary telescopes. However, the neutral hydrogen atom emits radio waves on a particular wavelength of 21 centimetres, and these interstellar hydrogen clouds can be detected and measured with the radio telescopes. The story of the detection of these 21-centimetre emissions is an epic of modern science. In the terrible circumstances of the German occupation Van de Hulst, a young research student in Holland, made the calculations which led him to predict the existence of these radio waves. He showed that although for any one hydrogen atom the process of emission is only likely to take place once in eleven million years, the numbers of atoms in the interstellar clouds are so great that the emission should be detectable. Years of peace were required to develop the right equipment, and then in 1951 these weak radio waves were detected—an event which represented a triumph of technical skill and a brilliant vindication of Van de Hulst's prediction.

The astronomers in Leiden under their director, Jan Oort, seized on this unparalleled opportunity of piercing the secrets of the structure of the Milky Way. The large optical telescopes are powerless to penetrate the interstellar dust clouds which obscure the structural details of the system—and you must remember that we are placed in an unprivileged position on the edge of the galactic disk. The dust presents little handicap to the passage of the 21-centimetre waves, and during the last few years Oort and his staff have produced results of almost unbelievable detail and elegance describing parts of the Milky Way which man will never see.

The second feature of the radio waves which come from within the confines of the Milky Way is that the smooth background of radio emission is punctuated by very strong sources which stand out for the radio telescope in the same way that the bright visual stars stand out from the diffuse light of the Milky Way. I have already emphasized that the common bright stars do not emit radio waves—at least they have not yet been detected—and the solution to the origin of these strong sources of radio waves cannot be found in the common stars. There are a few cases where these radio sources have been identified with unusual objects which can be seen in the optical telescopes. The most spectacular is the Crab Nebula, 4,000 light years away. This nebula is the gaseous remains of an exploding star or supernova outburst seen by Chinese astronomers 900 years ago in A.D. 1054. The millions of tons of hydrogenous material of the star disintegrated in a catastrophic explosion, and at present we see the gaseous shell of the explosion still moving out through space at the rate of 70 million miles a day. This gas is at a high temperature and in a great state of turmoil, and we believe that these conditions are responsible for the radio emission. There are two other well-established cases of supernova outbursts in the galactic system—those observed by Tycho Brahe in 1572 and by Kepler in 1604. The visible remnants of these are difficult to see in the telescopes, but both have been identified as radio sources.

The most powerful of the radio sources in the Milky Way lies in the constellation of Cassiopeia, and this was very difficult to link up with any visible object. A few years ago after protracted research the American astronomers on Palomar succeeded in photographing a strange object coincident with the radio source. It is a diffuse and faintly luminous region of gas covering an area of sky which is much larger than that occupied by a star. The object contains filaments of gas in extremely violent motion. Recently, less intense sources have been associated with similar regions of diffuse gas in Gemini and Auriga. No one yet knows where these stand in the sequence of stellar evolution; they may be old supernovae or, alternatively, the beginning of the concentrations of gas which ultimately form stars. One thing seems certain, they are so faint and diffuse that they are unlikely to have been recognized as significant stellar objects but for their strong radio emissions.

From these remarks you will see that the radio emission generated in the Milky Way system has complex origins, such as the diffuse regions of turbulent gas which give us localized radio sources, of which some at least are supernova; the clouds of neutral hydrogen gas; the corona around the system where no matter can be seen; and probably emission from ionized hydrogen which contributes to the background radiation. But when we inspect our records we find many thousands of radio sources which seem to be distributed uniformly over the sky. Most of these are much weaker than those which I have just described in relation to the Milky Way, and their uniform distribution leads us to believe that they are external and lie at great distances from the local galaxy. Of course, the extragalactic star systems, of which there may be a hundred or even a thousand million in the field of view of the large optical telescopes, have an overall uniform distribution in space—at least within the two thousand million light years to which the telescopes penetrate. It would therefore be natural to look for a close association between these nebulae and the radio sources.

When this is done, only a very limited number of associations can be found. The great spiral nebula in Andromeda at a distance of 2 million light years is one, but until a few months ago not more than a dozen out of all the millions of these normal extragalactic star systems had been related to the radio sources. This is entirely consistent with the strength of the radio waves emitted by the Milky Way system. If the extragalactic systems radiate in a similar way, then on account of their great distances from us only a small number would be detectable. The consistency of this picture has recently been firmly established by Hanbury Brown and Hazard using the new Jodrell Bank telescope with which they have been able to make detailed studies of several dozens of these normal extragalactic nebulae. Amongst all the confusion which still exists we can, I think, say that the spiral nebulae in the universe emit radio waves in the same way as our own spiral Milky Way system, but that very few of them can be detected with present day radio telescopes.

We are therefore still left with this problem of the thousands of radio sources which are detected by our radio telescopes, and we now believe that the solution of this puzzle may lie in one of the most remarkable of all the discoveries in radio astronomy. Some years ago Ryle and his colleagues in Cambridge made a very accurate measurement of the position of one of the stronger of these unidentified sources which lies in the constellation of Cygnus. These measurements were sufficiently accurate for the American astronomers to use the 200-inch telescope on Palomar to make an exhaustive search of this region of the sky. They found there a remarkable event in which two great extragalactic nebulae seem to have collided with one another. This collision, which is at a distance of 700 million light years, is nearly at the limit of clear definition of the world's biggest optical telescope, and yet the radio waves are relatively strong—so strong that even if the nebulae were ten times farther away we could still detect them as a radio source. We do not yet understand why two nebulae in collision like this produce radio waves which are far more intense than those they would produce separately. For our present argument the important fact is that the strength of the radio emission is out of all proportion to the visibility of the nebulae in the optical sense.

Nicholas Copernicus (1473-1543)

An early planetarium, called an orrery, for teaching the
Copernican system
(American Museum of Natural History)

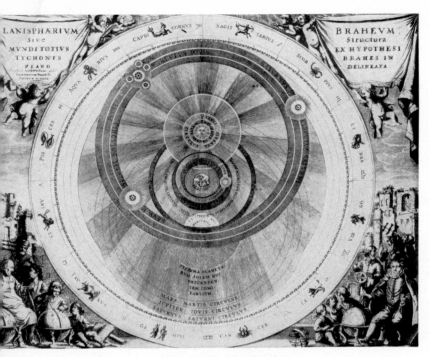

The planetary system according to Tycho Brahe
(American Museum of Natural History)

The Earl of Rosse's 72-inch telescope (1845)
(Radio Times Hulton Picture Library)

A meteorite which fell at Beddgelert, North Wales, in 1949
(By permission of the British Museum [Natural History])

The cluster of nebulae in Hydra. Distance about 360 million
light years.   *(Mount Wilson and Palomar Observatories)*

The 200-inch Hale telescope on Mount Palomar, California, the l[
est optical telescope in the world
(Mount Wilson and Palomar Observatories)

The radio telescop[
Jodrell Bank, Cheshire, Engl[
(Photo by A. F. H. Si[

A view of the Jodrell Bank reflector under construction gives a str[i]ing impression of its great size.
(Keystone)

The aerials of a big radio telescope being built by the
Russians at the Biurakan Observatory in Soviet Armenia
(Pix, Incorporated)

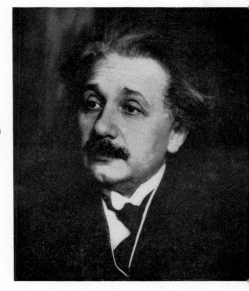

Albert Einstein (1879-1955)
(Radio Times Hulton Picture Library)

Sir Arthur Eddington
(1882-1944)
(British Information Services)

The solar corona observed at a total eclipse of the Sun at
Syd Koster, Sweden, in June, 1954
(Royal Greenwich Observatory)

Galaxy NGC 5128, which is associated with an intense radio source i
Centaurus; it is believed to represent the collision of two galaxies in
remote part of the Universe.
(Mount Wilson and Palomar Observatories)

luto: two photographs showing the motion of the planet in twenty-
our hours

Mount Wilson and Palomar Observatories)

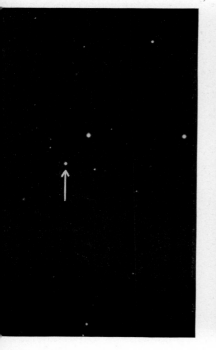

The Crab Nebula in Taurus, the remains of a supernova outburst
seen by Chinese astronomers in A.D. 1054
(Mount Wilson and Palomar Observatories)

The Spiral Nebula in Virgo, seen edge on
(Mount Wilson and Palomar Observatories)

The Great Nebula in Andromeda
(Mount Wilson and Palomar Observatories)

The relevance of this event to the problem of our unidentified radio sources depends on the question as to whether this collision of galaxies is unique. If one surveys the space around the Milky Way system, then it is very empty—there is not another galaxy of stars closer than a million or so light years, and this is a fairly average distance between galaxies. In this case the chances of collision are negligible. On the other hand, in the great clusters of galaxies which exist far out in space one might find a thousand galaxies separated by a mere thirty thousand light years. This still gives us a separation of a million million million miles between the galaxies and that, by ordinary standards, is a safe distance. But the galaxies in the clusters are moving about at a speed of over 2,000 miles a second, and this makes the chance of collision a substantial one.

We believe that the majority of these radio sources which lie outside the Milky Way may be colliding galaxies—a belief which has been strengthened by the discovery of a few more similar associations. We believe also that our failure to identify more of these radio sources with visible events arises because the collisions are taking place at very great distances, beyond the range of the optical telescopes. This view is now being freely discussed, but the precise interpretation of the current results from Cambridge and Sydney, where so much of this work has been done, is hotly disputed. The problem is of the very greatest significance to cosmology, and I must reserve further discussion until we consider the question of the origin of the universe.

On the issue of the collisions of galaxies I should perhaps say that I have adopted the interpretation which the American astronomers place on their own photographs. In the case of the two best examples in Cygnus and Perseus the photographs show the entwinement of two galactic systems. Ambartzumian, the distinguished Soviet astronomer, has argued that these are not collisions, but cases where the nucleus of a single galaxy has divided to form two separate systems, and that the photographs show the galaxies in process of separation. He believes that the parts of the divided nucleus are receding from one another with a speed of many hundreds of miles a second, and that very violent processes continue for tens of millions of years. The radio emission he believes to be a result of these violent processes involving the collision of masses of interstellar matter and the ejection of high-energy particles from the atmospheres of very young stars.

Earlier in this talk I referred to the great desire to find out what the universe is like beyond the present two thousand million light year limit of the optical telescopes, and it is natural to inquire if our present-day radio telescopes have yet penetrated to these remote regions of space and time. Unfortunately it is a question to which at present there is no decisive answer. One can, however, say this. If the interpretation of the unidentified radio sources which I have given during the last few minutes is correct, then some recent measurements of the strength and size of a few of those sources which have been made at Jodrell Bank implies that we are dealing with events at distances of many thousands of millions of light years. Indeed, we may now be in the process of probing the ultimate depths of space and time.

IV. Astronomy and the State

At the end of my last talk, I suggested that our modern telescopes might be approaching the limit of man's possible penetration into the depths of space. It would be natural to speak now about the nature and meaning of this vast universe which is revealed. Before I do this, I want to pause to consider a different question.

Until the seventeenth century the idea that astronomical theories could be subject to detailed observational tests was not generally accepted. The relation of the astronomer to society, the survival of his theories, and his personal safety, depended on the battle of the intellect. After Galileo and Newton the position changed entirely. In the overall progress of astronomy the intellectual strife diminished to the point of unimportance, and the practical life of the astronomer became more and more involved in the striving to obtain better instruments for observing the heavens.

In the 300 years which separated Galileo's small telescope from the telescopes on Mount Wilson and Palomar the astronomer depended largely on private sources for the ever-increasing cost of his instruments. The state was an interested but not particularly benevolent onlooker. Today we have entered a new phase. As I said last week, the Second World War stimulated technical developments for military purposes which, as a by-product, made possible the evolution of new observational tools for the astronomer in the form of radio astronomy and earth satellites. The interests of the State have become deeply involved, at least in the techniques, and very often in the results.

Although this situation is new, it is interesting to recall that official astronomy in Great Britain did owe its inception to the intervention of the State. The Royal Greenwich Observatory was founded in 1675 by King Charles the Second. Its purpose was to make such astronomical observations as would determine longitude at sea. However, the Observatory was not of much value to navigators until Harrison perfected the marine chronometer a hundred years later. In the meantime, the first Astronomer Royal, Flamsteed, followed by Halley and Bradley, carried through an extensive programme of fundamental work in astronomy. The demonstration that it was possible to determine longitude at sea was, of course, of immense value to shipping, and the Royal Observatory came under Admiralty control in 1820, where it still remains to this day.

This example may be thought to contradict my statement that the entwinement of astronomy with the State is of recent origin, but this is not so. Charles the Second asked Wren to build the Observatory at Greenwich and called Flamsteed to the post of Astronomer Royal. But Flamsteed equipped the Observatory with the help of benefactors and at his own expense. Herschel built his telescope privately, although his famous 48-inch instrument, which he built in 1785, was assisted by Royal patronage. The distinction gained by British astronomy on the basis of individual initiative and private enterprise was even more firmly established twenty years after Herschel's death when the Earl of Rosse succeeded in constructing his 72-inch telescope. At the time when Lord Rosse was already able to observe the spiral structure of distant nebulae there was no telescope of any significance on the American continent. In 1825, John Quincey Adams spoke before Congress: 'It is with no feeling of pride as an American,' he said, 'that the remark may be made that on the comparatively small territorial surface of Europe there are existing upward of one hundred and thirty of these lighthouses of the skies, while throughout the whole American hemisphere there is not one.'

Adams turned from a scornful and derisive Congress to raise money by public subscription, and the foundation of the great American observatories in this way was assisted by the fortunate appearance of Halley's Comet in 1835 and the great comet of 1843, which aroused people everywhere to the need for better telescopes. The American astronomical scene has been dominated almost entirely until the last few years by private benefactions. The succession of telescopes of ever-increasing size by which American astronomers have captured the initiative in astronomical research were built because George Ellery Hale had the vision and ability to obtain very large sums of money without state assistance. Yerkes, Carnegie, and Hooker responded to his requests, and then in 1928 came Hale's greatest achievement when he obtained from the Rockefeller Foundation six million dollars for the construction of the 200-inch telescope which now operates on Palomar Mountain. Much of the contemporary picture of the universe has arisen from the operation of these wonderful instruments. The dominating influence of private benefactions in the field of large astronomical telescopes on the American continent has, in the past, been almost complete. In fact, only one large telescope —the 120-inch at Lick Observatory, which is not yet in action—has been financed otherwise.

A century after Adam's abortive approach to Congress the relative position of British and American astronomy was almost completely reversed. With relatively small private benefaction and even less state assistance, no one in Great Britain could build a successor to Lord Rosse's telescope. It is, indeed, a mortifying thought that the largest telescope in Great Britain today is considerably smaller than the telescope which Herschel built in 1785, and that the majority of the telescopes at the Royal Observatory date from the nineteenth century. In a year when America has added to her astronomical riches by granting over two million dollars for the creation of a new National Optical Observatory in New Mexico, and Russia has announced her intention of building a 236-inch telescope, the construction of a 100-inch British telescope has been postponed because of financial difficulties.

The steady decay of British influence in astronomy has fortunately been arrested by remarkable developments in the technical field. In my last lecture I described the new epoch which we have entered through the science of radio astronomy. The radio telescopes which have made possible these developments are expensive to build and operate. Great Britain has spent over a million pounds on such instruments during the last few years. In America, after a reluctant start, fifteen million dollars (or more than five million pounds) have already been invested in similar radio telescopes, and by 1962 a single radio telescope built by one of the American armed services will have cost more than one hundred million dollars. A survey of the international scene in astronomy gives me excitement and pleasure as an astronomer, but as a citizen, I am filled with dismay. The American enterprises in this new subject are now being pursued with such vigour that they seem likely to establish precedence over our own efforts within a few years. In fact, the history of the developments of optical telescopes in the two countries may soon be repeated in these new fields of endeavour.

Neither is it possible for me to derive any sense in patriotic satisfaction from a study of the development of astronomy in the U.S.S.R. For over 200 years the Academy of Sciences has played a prominent role in the encouragement of astronomy in Russia. The famous Pulkovo Observatory near Leningrad, established in 1839, was frequently regarded as the astronomical capital of the world in the nineteenth century. But Pulkovo and the other large observatory at Simeiz in the Crimea were razed to the ground during the battles of the Second World War. Thirteen years ago, when the American telescopes were in the full flood of discovery, not a single coherent group of astronomers with any worthwhile equipment existed in Russia. When viewed against this grim background, the recovery of the astronomical sciences must be regarded as phenomenal. Pulkovo and Simeiz have been rebuilt and extended, and at least six other major observatories have been created during the last decade. During the years when Great Britain has cast on one side the construction of the 100-inch telescope, the U.S.S.R. has proceeded with the 100-inch in the Crimea, and has announced its plans for building a telescope even larger than the 200-inch at Palomar. Radio telescopes of great size are now coming into use, and the determination with which these new techniques are being pursued by large teams of technicians and astronomers is a clear indication of the concern of the U.S.S.R. with the fundamental problems of science, at a time when, indeed, it might well justify the use of its resources for other purposes of more immediate human concern.

Whereas the recovery of Soviet astronomy from such disasters is a matter for admiration, the development of a completely new technique of astronomical observation in the form of an earth satellite has made the world gasp with astonishment. With the interest centred on the American proposals to launch an earth satellite as part of its International Geophysical Year programme, the Soviet Union scored a major triumph by the successful launching of Sputnik One on 4 October, 1957, followed a few weeks later by the even greater accomplishment of orbiting Sputnik Two, weighing over a ton and packed with scientific instruments. Now, the avowed purpose of earth satellites is for geophysical and astronomical observations, and only those of a conservative outlook would deny the enormous advantages of astronomical investigations made above the absorbing and disturbing regions of the terrestrial atmosphere. However, the cost of such enterprises is, by any standards, very great, and it is now well known that the launching rockets of the satellites, which represent the main cost, are military weapons of most devastating potential.

It seems unlikely that without the practical and military urge behind these developments the scientists of Russia and America would today be in a position to use these new astronomical tools. It is almost impossible to form any reliable estimate of the cost of the satellite programmes, because so much of the work is borne on the defence budgets. The ill-fated Vanguard programme in the U.S.A. has cost about a hundred and twenty million dollars. Less than a quarter of this sum has gone into the actual satellite part of the programme, such as the manufacture of the satellite and its instruments, with the associated tracking and computing systems. But this must be a small part of the sum already spent in the U.S.A. on the programmes which led to the successful launching of the Explorer satellites and lunar probes. The only guide we have is the statement that in the fiscal year 1959 expenditures for missiles procurement are estimated at over three thousand million dollars, which is five times the rate of expenditure for this purpose as recently as fiscal year 1955. After the successful test of the British experimental ballistic weapon known as Black Knight in September, which is capable of forming only one part of a satellite launching rocket, the cost of its development was given as five million pounds sterling, and that of the associated rocket range at Woomera as fifty million pounds. It is therefore clear that in these new fields of work we are dealing with an expenditure on an unprecedented scale, in which an experimental test of only a few minutes may cost more than the largest telescope yet built.

Those concerned with the astronomical sciences are therefore faced with an entirely new situation. It is understandable that some astronomers, brought up in the tradition of the peaceful isolation of the observatory dome under the starlit sky, do not receive with enthusiasm these new developments, in which their instruments are launched from the rocket range under the glare of publicity. Others are happy to join in the initiation of this new era of observation which would be impossible but for the political and military divisions of the world which have forced the governments to an expenditure which would never be borne as a budget for fundamental scientific work alone.

The brilliant successes of the U.S.S.R. in this work contrasted sharply with the initial difficulties of the U.S.A., and it is a question of much importance to determine why the roles of these nations both pursuing the same ends were so unexpectedly reversed. In this connexion one is struck most forcibly by the relative positions of the scientists and engineers in the U.S.S.R. and the West. During the vital years of the development of these projects American science was under the shadow of a Secretary of Defence who could see little value in research which had no immediate foreseeable economic or commercial value.

The relevant branches of American science were understaffed, uncorrelated, and without the necessary finance to such an extent that General James Gavin and others resigned in protest. By contrast, the power of the Academy of Sciences in Russia is very great. The essential factor appears to be that the initiation of scientific projects is determined by the desire of the scientists of the Academy and that the financial restrictions which place such grave handicaps on the Western scientists do not exist. The single-minded purpose behind such developments, which are carried through with human welfare taking second place, is a feature which has no parallel in Western life. The direct and continuous communication between the Council of Ministers and the senior Academicians determines that no human frailties or vacillations shall interfere with this unity of purpose. As a result, we see today a scientific and technological nation in the early stages of development which already has great ability and power. In all events of the past year I find few things more symbolic than the ease with which the U.S.S.R. launched Sputnik One, weeks ahead of schedule.

It is ironical that the precedence which Russia established in this way appeared to be the one factor required to transform the American situation. At last money became of secondary importance, the divisions were at least partially healed in a fanatic drive to establish parity, and the recent creation of the National Aeronautics and Space Administration with an actual budget this year of three hundred million dollars, and a projected budget of a thousand million dollars in two years' time, gives a new and refreshing sense of well-being and unity to the American astronomical space projects. The deplorable nature of the competition which has led to this transformation has hastened the development of space research beyond anything which was conceivable a few years ago.

Why are the Great Powers willing to spend so much money on these astronomical projects, so that a few privileged scientists can study the regions of space outside the immediate environment of the earth? The answer to this question is certainly not obvious as it would be, for example, in the case of the investigations of an atomic scientist. There the easy answer is in terms of national survival, economically in terms of power resources, and militarily in terms of bombs. No one today would deny that the most recondite investigation of the structure of atoms might some day influence the development of atomic power or bombs. On the other hand, it may be difficult to see why the study of the structure of a remote nebula could have any relation to the practical business of the State.

The fundamental answer to this general question is written large in history. It is a matter of deep concern

that succeeding generations have so often had to redis-
cover it for themselves—often by bitter experience.
The technical devices which form the basis of the present economic and cultural strength of the Great Powers
can be traced back within a few generations to fundamental scientific investigations which were carried out
in the abstract, supported without thought of direct
practical benefit. Without pause, one thinks of the class-
ical linkages of the investigations of Faraday with
electrical power, Clerk Maxwell with radio communi-
cations, and Rutherford with atomic power.

Now, it is not part of my daily job to seek any possible
practical outcome of my work; and the large sums of
money which have been given for radio telescopes in
this country were invested in faith for the free investigation of the universe. But the first use of the telescope
which was conceived and built to study the universe
was the detection and tracking by radar of the launching rocket of the Russian sputnik. I do not think one
could wish for a more dramatic answer to the question
which I posed just now.[1] May I give yet another example.

[1] *At this point in his broadcast Professor Lovell introduced a recording
with these words:* Another example. Here is a note of the American lunar
probe, Pioneer, as it was picked up by the telescope a few weeks ago when
it was nearly 80,000 miles away in space. . . .
*The recording played during the lecture was made during the flight of
the American lunar probe, Pioneer, on 11/12 October 1958. In this operation the radio telescope was used as a receiving system in order to pick up
the beacon transmitter carried in the probe. The telescope had two main
functions. First, to plot the position of the probe during its flight and pass*

One of my young research students, John Evans, was assigned the task of studying the surface of the moon by radar. He sent out a pulse of radio waves every few seconds and measured their strength when they were reflected back to the radio telescope after their 2½-second return journey to the moon. Although the transmitted signal was always the same strength, the signal which came back from the moon varied very rapidly in strength.[1] Evans made a mathematical analysis of these variations and reached the surprising conclusion that his signals were being reflected only from a small area on the forward hemisphere of the moon. Now we did not start this investigation for any practical purpose, but the result implied that the moon could be used as a space relay for transatlantic radio communication; this would be a way of overcoming the

---

the information to the computing center in Los Angeles; secondly, to record on magnetic tape the modulation on the beacon signal (the telemetry), which contained all the information about the scientific experiments carried in the probe.

In the Sputnik experiment the telescope has been used as a radar instrument, that is, pulses of radio waves were transmitted from the telescope and picked up again after scattering from the Sputnik or carrier rocket. This type of experiment is extremely difficult because of the small scattering area of the target, its speed of motion, and uncertainty of its position. Apart from the occasions when it can be seen visually by reflected sunlight, this radar technique is the only way to obtain information about the target once the beacon signals have ceased, or if no beacon is carried (e.g., in the case of the carrier rocket).

[1] *Professor Lovell went on:* Here is a record of the moon echoes. First you have the transmitted pulse, then immediately afterwards the moon echo, which you will be able to recognize easily because of its relative difference in strength. . . .

severe hindrances occasioned by radio fadeouts in the more conventional method.[1] It would be unwise to oversimplify the complex issues at stake in these mat-

[1] *Professor Lovell went on:* Earlier this week we tried to make a recording to prove to you that our voices transmitted by radio to the moon and back remained perfectly intelligible. Unfortunately we only had a very small transmitter, and the echoed voice is weak. But you may just be able to hear the 'hullo' coming back after its 2½-second return journey through the quarter of a million miles to the moon. First you will hear the 'hullo' and then after 2½ seconds the faint echo superimposed on a great deal of noise. . . . Incidentally, that background noise is the radio waves from the universe which I talked about last week. I'm sorry the echo was so weak, but that's not really important. After all, our transmitter had only a thousandth of the power of some of the transmitters which are broadcasting my voice now. The important point is that the voice when received back from the moon is perfectly intelligible and that the telescope was working on wavelengths which could never be disturbed by atmospheric or ionospheric conditions. Well, the result of that investigation is a free gift of the radio astronomer, to all the commercial and military organizations who will no doubt use it in the future.

Two recordings were played to illustrate this part of the lecture. In the first one the actual pulses of radio waves transmitted through the radio telescope were made audible, and the pulse received after scattering from the lunar surface was recorded 2½ seconds later. The transmitted pulse was always the same strength, but the received pulse varied in strength. This 'rapid fading' of the moon echoes is caused by the libration or apparent rocking motion of the moon relative to the earth. The correlation between the strengths of the successive reflected pulses can be used to investigate the nature of the scattering. When these calculations are made it is found that the scattering must be taking place only from a small area on the forward hemisphere of the moon, and not from the whole of the forward hemisphere, as might be expected. As a consequence, a short pulse of radio waves is reflected as a short pulse and not distorted as it would be if reflection occurred from the whole hemisphere. Similarly, it is to be expected that speech would remain reasonably coherent when reflected from the moon, and not distorted into unintelligibility as it would be otherwise. The second recording demonstrated this fact. A small transmitter and receiver were mounted in the swinging laboratory underneath the bowl of the telescope, which was under control to track the moon continuously. The

ters, but it is obviously easier, on the one hand, to present the case for expenditure on fundamental scientific research, and on the other, for the State to justify the expenditure to the taxpayer when the techniques, and possibly some of the results, have close associations with a wide range of activities outside the scientist's laboratory.

The expenditure of large sums of money by the State on fundamental scientific research, although inevitable, is full of long-term dangers. In my second lecture I gave an example of the restriction of free astronomical inquiry in Russia today. In Great Britain the dangers are enhanced by the difficult and peculiar situation which exists in the Universities. The great scientists of the past were able to achieve their tremendous successes with so little expense that the University organizations have grown up without difficulty on the

---

transmitter was modulated in the conventional way by speaking into a microphone, and the receiver picked up the 'voice echo' from the moon 2½ seconds later. The telescope was used both for the transmission and reception of the signals, although, of course, there is no reason why the transmission and reception should not be carried out at quite separate sites, e.g., across the Atlantic, always provided that the moon is above the horizon at both sites. The demonstration was made on a wavelength of 75 cm., on which wavelength there is no possibility of disturbances from the atmosphere or ionosphere. Normal transatlantic radio communication has to be made on much longer wavelengths, which are reflected from the ionosphere and are therefore subject to fade-outs and other disturbances. In the demonstration the voice echo was perfectly intelligible although weak. The transmitter used had a power output of only 70 watts, and the signal strength could be increased readily by using a more powerful transmitter.

basis of reasonable equality of expenditure as between arts and science. The problem of absorbing the vast new instruments of science in conventional University departments is exceedingly difficult, and in fact the desirability of doing so is in question because of the fear of destroying the traditional balance of activities. It seems to me that those charged with the administration of the Universities in Great Britain are today faced with a delicate and perilous situation which is without precedent. A failure to absorb these great new scientific projects into a framework where the traditional university freedom of inquiry can flourish will be fraught with grave dangers to scholarship and scientific education.

In America the dangers at present are of a different kind. The financing of the radio astronomical projects is already heavily biased by the investments of the armed services, and early in the next decade when the 600-foot telescope is available it seems likely that these investments by the military authorities will dominate the American radio astronomical scene. At present the demands of the services for specialized work from these groups of scientists is small. There is, indeed, no reason for it to be otherwise, since the lines of work likely to be pursued with these telescopes by the free volition of the scientists is of great fundamental interest to the services. However, this may not always be so. I am unable to discover any safeguards which would enable this vast fabric of fundamental astronomical research to survive a change of emphasis or opinion in the armed services concerned. It is indeed fortunate that so far in Great Britain these new developments have been contained within a University framework where freedom is a prized and jealously guarded possession.

The main concern of the astronomer is with highly abstract and remote topics. Some of this work can still be pursued by the astronomers working in isolation from the daily turmoil of existence. But we are moving into a new epoch in which even the study of the remote parts of the universe demand a close partnership between the astronomer and the State. The instruments which are destined to solve the problems of the origin of the universe may well rise from the rocket range. The pursuit of the good and the evil are now linked in astronomy as in almost all science.

In so far as Great Britain is concerned I have tried to show that the recovery of our heritage in the astronomical sciences is in acute danger, and that the peril lies deep in our national well-being. The pessimists say that we cannot compete and that within the next decade the scientific and technological superiority of the U.S.S.R. over the West will be complete. I do not believe that this will necessarily be the case, because I think that the restraints on freedom which I discussed earlier may reduce the effectiveness of Russian science, and may counteract to some extent their enormous superiority in scientific man-power and finance. On the other hand, one thing seems beyond contention. Fundamental research in astronomy or any other subject is an essential component in the welfare of modern civilization. Unless the West overcomes its present parsimonious attitude to science and technology, then the relative quality of our civilization will decline, and our influence will pass to other peoples. I have referred to the great sums now being spent, particularly in the U.S.A., but in so far as they support research, these represent a quite negligible proportion of the national budget. Neither in Great Britain nor the U.S.A. have we yet provided the facilities to saturate our existing scientific man-power. Therein lie my grounds for personal pessimism. Moreover, our danger rests, not in our limited potential, but in those amongst us who think of science and astronomy in terms of the sacrifice of a television set or motor car today so that our grandchildren can get to the moon. Alas, the issues at stake are of a different order of gravity. The fate of human civilization will depend on whether the rockets of the future carry the astronomer's telescope or a hydrogen bomb.

V. The Origin of the Universe—I

In this lecture and the next I want to talk to you
about the problem of the origin of the universe. I sup-
pose it would hardly be an exaggeration to say that this
is the greatest challenge to the intellect which faces
man, and I cannot pretend that I have any new solution to offer you. However, you may have gathered
from my earlier talks that today the air is alive with
a new hope and expectancy, because our new instruments may be reaching out so far into space that we
may soon be able to speak with more confidence. I am
going to set out the problem as I see it, and I hope
you will get an idea of these vast cosmological issues and
of the implications of the alternative solutions which
lie ahead. At the end I shall tell you what I think about
it all as an ordinary human being.

We have seen that observational astronomy tells us
about the universe as it exists out to distances of about
two thousand million light years. At that distance we
are seeing the universe as it existed two thousand

million years ago. Within this vast area of space and time we can study the innumerable stars and galaxies, and from these observations we can attempt to infer the probable nature and extent of the cosmos beyond the range of observations.

I think there are three stages in which we might consider this problem. The first stage is to inquire whether the observations are likely to be extended in the future to even greater distances and thereby penetrate even farther into past history than the present two thousand million years. The second stage is an appeal to cosmological theory, an inquiry as to the extent to which the present observations agree with any particular cosmology and the nature of the past and future as predicted by these theories. Finally, we shall reach a stage where theories based on our present conceptions of physical laws have nothing further to say. At this point we pass from physics to metaphysics, from astronomy to theology, where the corporate views of science merge into the beliefs of the individual.

The vast region of space and time enclosed by the present observations includes several hundred million galaxies of stars. As far as we can see, the overall large-scale structure of the universe within these limits has a high degree of uniformity. When we look at these distant regions we find that the light is reddened, indicating that the galaxies are receding from us. As far as we can see, the red shift of the most distant nebulae is still increasing linearly with distance. There is no indication that we are seeing anything but a small part of the total universe. However, in the second stage of our inquiry we shall see that an observational test between rival cosmological theories demands a still further penetration, and an extension of the present observational limit is a matter of some urgency in cosmology. Unfortunately there are fundamental difficulties introduced by the recession of the galaxies which no device of man will ever surmount. At the present observable limit of the large optical telescopes the galaxies are receding with a speed of about one-fifth of the velocity of light. From this aspect alone we face a limit to future progress. Even if no other effects intervened we could never obtain information about those farther regions of space where the velocities of recession of the galaxies reach the speed of light. The light from the more distant galaxies will never reach us. In Eddington's phrase 'Light is like a runner on an expanding track with the winning post receding faster than he can run.'

There are, moreover, further difficulties which will hinder the approach to this fundamental limit. If the remote galaxies were stationary, then all the light emitted, say, in one second would reach our telescopes. But the galaxies are moving away with speeds which are an appreciable fraction of the velocity of light, and as the speed increases less and less of the light actually

emitted by the galaxies in one second reaches our instruments. This degradation of the intensity of the
light coupled with the accompanying shift in wavelength to the red end of the spectrum worsens still
further the technical difficulties of these observations.

The radio telescopes may well be in a stronger position with respect to these hindrances. To begin with,
the collisions of galaxies, which I described in an earlier
lecture, generate very powerful radio emissions, and
the shifts in wavelength which accompany the recession
do not present the same observational difficulties as in
the optical case. In fact, the present belief is that many
of the objects already studied by their radio emissions
lie at distances which exceed considerably the present
two thousand million light years' limit of the optical
telescopes. Therefore, we can, I think, answer the first
stage of our inquiry with some degree of certainty
in the following way. The present observable horizon
of the universe will be pushed back by a limited amount
in the near future, perhaps to a few thousand million
light years. Then we must be content. No further
strivings or inventions of man will enable us to probe
the conditions which existed in epochs of history beyond
these few thousand million years. They are gone for
ever beyond the fundamental limits of observability.

At this point we reach the second stage of our inquiry,
where we appeal to cosmological theory. The question
is this. Can we formulate a theory in terms of known

physical laws whose predictions agree so well with the present observable universe that we can predict the past and future?

Indeed, when we turn to the cosmological theories which are today seriously considered by astronomers we find a most absorbing state of affairs. Not one, but several theories can explain from acceptable postulates the present observable state of the universe. These predictions bring us face to face with the ultimate problem of the origin of the universe in ways which are startlingly different. But the new techniques in astronomy may be on the verge of producing observational data which may be decisively in favour of one or other of these cosmologies. At least one of these alternatives would, I think, present theology with a very serious dilemma. In fact, if the full implications of the theory eventually receive the support of astronomical observations it is difficult to see how certain fundamental doctrines could be maintained in their present harmonious relation with our physical knowledge of the universe.

First of all, though, I want to discuss the cosmological theories which are generally classed as the evolutionary models of the universe. I think it would be correct to say that these theories, which are a consequence of Einstein's general theory of relativity, are regarded with the most favour by the majority of contemporary astronomers. In passing, perhaps I should add that in the light of our present knowledge it does not seem worth while discussing for our present purpose any of the cosmological theories which preceded the introduction of the theory of general relativity in 1915. The application of Newton's theory of gravitation, in which the attraction between bodies varies inversely as the square of their distance apart, to the large-scale structure of the universe would require that the universe had a centre in which the spatial density of stars and galaxies was a maximum. As we proceed outwards from this centre the spatial density should diminish, until finally at great distances it should be succeeded by an infinite region of emptiness. The observed uniformity in the large-scale structure of the universe is clearly at variance with these ideas. Neither does any theory based on Newton's laws of universal attraction and conservation of mass offer hope of explaining the observed expansion and recession of the nebulae. On the other hand, in Einstein's theory of general relativity gravitation is not explained in terms of a force but of the deformation of space near massive bodies. In our ordinary life we treat space as though it were flat, or Euclidean, in the sense that the geometrical properties obey the axioms of Euclid as we were taught in school. For example, the three angles of a triangle add up to two right angles. According to Einstein's theory, however, these simple conceptions must be abandoned, and though in ordinary circumstances the differences are insignificant, nevertheless when we consider the properties of space near a massive star, for example, the conceptions of a flat space no longer apply.

If we could construct a sufficiently large triangle under these conditions we should find that the three angles no longer added up to two right angles. In fact, the situation would be similar to the triangle formed by three curved lines drawn on the surface of a sphere. The basic conceptions of Einstein's theory were quickly verified by the discovery that it could account for the previously inexplicable perturbations in the motion of the planet Mercury as it approached the sun, and by the discovery that the light rays from a distant star when viewed so that it was nearly in line with the sun were deflected by the sun's gravitational field.

Einstein attempted to apply his new ideas of the gravitational curvature of space-time to the universe as a whole. In this case the curvature of space would be influenced not only by one star, but by countless stars and galaxies. However, in the large-scale view, as we have seen, the distribution has a high degree of uniformity, and the problem of the overall curvature of space can be related to the average density of the matter in the universe. In working out the equations Einstein was unable to find any solution which described a static universe. We must remember that this was a decade before the discovery of the recession of the nebulae, and any cosmological theory which did not provide for a static cosmos could have been little more than a curiosity.

Faced with this dilemma, Einstein realized in 1917 that the difficulties could be surmounted by the introduction of a new term in his equations. This is the famous λ term, or the cosmical constant, over which there was to be so much future dispute. This new term appears in the equations as an arbitrary universal constant. Its interpretation in terms of a physical model of the universe is that it introduces an effect analogous to repulsion. This cosmic repulsion increases with the distance between bodies, and is to be regarded as superimposed on the usual forces of Newtonian attraction. Thus at great distances the repulsion outweighs the attraction, and in the equilibrium condition the Newtonian attraction and cosmical repulsion are in exact balance.

We cannot follow in detail the subsequent developments, which are of the utmost complexity. Some years after the introduction of these ideas the whole situation was altered in dramatic fashion by the discovery that the universe was non-static but was expanding. At about the same time the Russian mathematician, Friedman, found other solutions of Einstein's equations which predicted either an expanding or contracting universe. In fact, now it has for long been realized that the equations of general relativity cannot define an unique universe because there are three unknowns in the equations, whereas observationally we have only two sets of data. The possible types of non-static universes fall into three main families determined by the various possible combinations of the sign of the cosmical constant and the space curvature. These are a universe which starts from a point origin at a finite time in the past and expands continuously to become infinitely large after an infinite time, a universe whose radius has a certain finite value at the initial moment of time, and thence expands to become infinite after an infinite time, and lastly a universe which expands from zero radius to a certain maximum and then collapses to zero again, this process of oscillation being capable of indefinite repetition. Within each of these three main categories a large number of possible models can be constructed differing in various points of detail. For the past thirty years cosmologists have sought for arguments based on the observed characteristics of the universe which would identify the actual universe with one of the theoretical models.

All that I propose to do here is to give some examples of these evolutionary models, one of which is today believed by many cosmologists to describe the past history with some degree of certainty. The first example is a solution discovered by the Abbé Lemaître in 1927 and developed by Eddington. I have already said that by introducing the cosmical constant Einstein was able to specify a static condition of the universe in which the Newtonian attraction and cosmical repulsion are in exact balance. However, this equilibrium is unstable. If something upsets the balance so that the attraction is weakened, then cosmical repulsion has the upper hand and an expansion begins. As the material of the universe separates, the distance between the bodies becomes greater, the attraction still further weakens, the cosmical repulsion ever increases, and the expansion becomes faster. On the other hand, if the equilibrium was upset in the other way so that the forces of attraction became superior, then the reverse would occur and the system would contract continuously. Eddington's view was that in the initial stage the universe consisted of a uniform distribution of protons and electrons, by our standards very diffuse. This proton-electron gas comprised the entire primeval universe, which would have had a radius of about a thousand million light years. At some stage an event or series of events must have occurred in this diffuse gas which determined that the universe was launched on a career of expansion and not contraction. There were many views as to how this might have happened. Eddington held that the accumulation of irregularities in the gas started the evolutionary tendency. Soon, condensations formed in the gas and those ultimately became the galaxies of stars. On these views the present radius of the universe must be about five times that of the initial static primeval universe.

In the light of modern knowledge this theory receives little support. The time scale of its evolution is too short, and one cannot find a compelling reason why the primeval gas should have been disturbed in such a way as to determine that the universe was launched on a career of expansion rather than contraction. The initial condition is a special case, ephemeral and fortuitous. As far as the laws of physics are concerned, one can only say that by chance the initial disturbances were such as to determine the history of the universe. One cannot feel very happy that such a chance occurrence some thousands of millions of years ago should have determined the fundamental features of the universe. Moreover, although originally the theory as expounded by Jeans and Eddington undoubtedly had attractive features for some theologians, I feel now that this might well have been enhanced by feelings of relief that the vastness, uniformity, and organization of the universe which had just been revealed still remained outside the conceivable laws of physics in its initial state. Indeed, when considering these initial conditions Jeans spoke in terms of 'the finger of God agitating the ether', implying a divine intervention at a predictable time in past history after which the laws of physics became applicable. This degree of familiarity with divine processes is, I think, undesirable theologically, and for science it evades the problem by obscuring the ultimate cosmological issue.

Moreover, there is another problem which must be

faced. The event which we have considered in the unstable static assemblage of primeval gas predetermined
the subsequent history of the universe. One must still
inquire how long the gas existed in this condition of
unstable equilibrium and how the primeval gas
originated. Science has nothing to say on this issue.
Indeed, it seems that the theory requires the exercise
of yet another divine act at some indeterminate time
before the occurrence which set off the gas on its career
of condensation and expansion.

Of course, this particular model is now of little more
than historical interest as being one of the first of the
evolutionary theories based on general relativity to receive serious attention. It provides, however, a remarkable example of the influence in cosmology of the
predilection of the individual. When faced with the
various possible cosmological models which we have
outlined, Eddington said this: 'Since I cannot avoid
introducing this question of a beginning, it has seemed
to me that the most satisfactory theory would be one
which made the beginning not too unaesthetically
abrupt. This condition can only be satisfied by an Einstein universe with all the major forces balanced.' He
continues, 'Perhaps it will be objected that, if one looks
far enough back, this theory does not really dispense
with an abrupt beginning, the whole universe must
come into being at one instant in order that it may start
in balance. I do not regard it in that way. To my mind

undifferentiated sameness and nothingness cannot be distinguished philosophically.' In this way Eddington attempted to rationalize the basis on which to build the universe.

I have already mentioned the Abbé Lemaître. His original work in 1927, published in a little-known journal, was discovered by Eddington. Although Eddington remained faithful to this idea that the universe evolved from the static but unstable Einstein universe, the conception was soon abandoned by Lemaître himself. For the past twenty-five years Lemaître's name has been associated with another model whose origin recedes even farther back in time than the static Einstein state. Of all cosmologies, it is, perhaps, by far the most thoroughly studied. We shall see later that during the last few years a tremendous clash has occurred with other opinions, but at the present time there are no known features of the observable universe which are incompatible with Lemaître's evolutionary cosmology. Lemaître's model is typical of one of the groups of theories inherent in general relativity, according to which the universe originated at a finite time in the past and expands to an infinite size at an infinite future time.

Perhaps we can most easily visualize this conception by taking the universe as we see it now and inquiring quite simply what might have been the situation long ago. The observations of the distant galaxies show that their light and radio emission is shifted in wavelength so that as received on the earth the light is redder and the radio waves longer in wavelength than those which are actually emitted. The interpretation of this shift is that we are separating from the galaxies at a very high speed, and that the speed of recession increases as we move out into space. At the limits of present-day observation the speed of recession is about thirty-seven thousand miles per second, which is a fifth of the velocity of light. The observation which gives us this figure is of a cluster of galaxies in Hydra photographed in the two-hundred-inch telescope. The so-called cosmological principle which is inherent in Lemaître's theory implies that if human beings equipped with similar instruments existed on a planet in this Hydra cluster of galaxies, then they would see the cluster of galaxies to which we belong at the limit of their powers of observation, and the velocity of recession would also be thirty-seven thousand miles per second. It is important to rid ourselves of any idea that because all around us we find galaxies in recession, then we are the centre of the recessional movement. This is not the case. It is an impression which we obtain because we can see only a small part of the total universe.

To return to this cluster of galaxies in Hydra. We are now seeing it as it was two thousand million years ago moving away at a rate of thirty-seven thousand miles a second. What is the likely past history of this and all other similar galaxies? Up to a point this question is not too difficult to answer. For example, a minute ago we were two million miles closer to this cluster than we are now. A year ago we were over a billion miles closer. If we recede back into history in this manner we realize that the galaxies such as Hydra which are now almost beyond our view must have been very much closer to us in the remote past. In fact, if we proceed in this way, then we reach a time of about eight or nine thousand million years ago when all the galaxies must have been very close together indeed. Of course, the galaxies themselves have evolved during this time, but the primeval material from which they were formed must have existed in a space which is very small compared with the universe today.

With important reservations which I shall deal with now, this in essence is the fundamental concept of Lemaître's theory, namely, that the universe originated from a dense and small conglomerate which Lemaître calls the primeval atom. I shall return in a moment to the conditions which might have existed at the beginning, and to the possible events which might have initiated the disruption and expansion of the primeval atom. It is in fact necessary to emphasize that the theory does not demand the formation of the galaxies in the first phase of the expansion. The primeval atom contained the entire material of the universe, and its density must have been inconceivably high—at least a hundred million tons per cubic centimetre. The initial momentum of the expansion dispersed this material, and after thousands of millions of years the conditions applicable to the so-called Einstein universe would have been reached. Then the size of the universe was about a thousand million light years and the density would have been comparable to that with which we are familiar on earth. According to Lemaître, at this stage the initial impetus of the expansion was nearly exhausted and the universe began to settle down into the nearly static condition which we have previously considered, where the forces of gravitational attraction and cosmical repulsion were in balance. The mathematical treatment indicates that the universe must have stayed for a long time in this condition. It is during this phase that the great clusters of galaxies began to form from the primeval material. Then the conditions of near equilibrium were again upset, the forces of cosmical repulsion began to win over those of gravitational attraction, and the universe was launched on the career of expansion which after nine thousand million years brought it to the state which we witness today.

The time scale determined by tracing back the past history of the galaxies brings us not to the beginning of time and space, but merely to a condition which existed a few thousand million years ago when the universe was probably about one-tenth of its present size and consisted of the original gaseous clouds from which the clusters of galaxies began to form. The processes of the formation and evolution of the galaxies from this early stage are the subject of very detailed mathematical treatment. There is, at present, every reason to believe that a satisfactory explanation of the evolution of the universe from that condition can be given in terms of the known laws of physics. But when we pass on to consider the even earlier stages, difficulties and uncertainties appear. How much farther do we have to go back in time to the condition of the primeval atom? The theory does not determine this with any precision, because the delay which the universe suffered during the equilibrium phase when the gaseous clouds were forming into galaxies cannot be specified. One can, however, say this—that the explosion or disintegration of the primeval atom must have occurred between twenty thousand million and sixty thousand million years ago. In other words the period of about nine thousand million years ago, when the galaxies began to form and the present period of expansion began, represents a comparatively recent phase in the history of the universe.

In my next and last lecture I shall talk about the alternative view which science can offer on the origin of the universe, but before doing this I want to dwell a moment on the implications of this evolutionary theory. The time scale, although vast, is conceivable in human terms. From the initial moment of time when the primeval atom disintegrated, astronomy and mathematics can attempt to describe the subsequent history of the universe to the state which we observe today. Moreover, there is every chance that in the foreseeable future man will produce experimental tests which will either substantiate or destroy this picture. But when we inquire what the primeval atom was like, how it disintegrated and by what means and at what time it was created we begin to cross the boundaries of physics into the realms of philosophy and theology. The important thing at that stage is what you and I think about this situation, this beginning of all time and space.

As a scientist I cannot discuss this problem of the creation of the primeval atom because it precedes the moment when I can ever hope to infer from observations the conditions which existed. If, indeed, the universe began in this way, then the concepts of space and time with which we deal originated at some moment between twenty thousand million and sixty thousand million years ago. Time, in the sense of being measured by any clock, did not exist before that moment, and space, in the sense of being measured by any yardstick, was contained entirely within the primeval atom. The vast regions of space which we survey today are just a small part of those which were originally the space of that small conglomerate.

We can, of course, speculate on the issues of the

creation of the primeval atom and its initial condition, but it is the philosopher who must first build a scheme which is self-consistent and which leads us smoothly into beginning of space-time where the mathematician can take over. Or one can simply refuse to discuss the question. If we wish to be materialistic, then we adopt the same attitude of mind as the materialist adopts in more common situations. The materialist will begin in the present case at the initiation of space-time when the primeval atom disintegrated. That quite simply evades the problem, and in my last lecture I shall describe some alternative theories and the kind of framework which might eventually form a metaphysical scheme before the beginning of time and space.

VI. The Origin of the Universe—II

IN MY LAST lecture I described one of the evolutionary theories of the origin of the universe. According to this theory, all the material of the universe and all of time and space were originally concentrated in a super-dense primeval atom which disintegrated about twenty or sixty thousand million years ago. During the course of this lecture I shall describe the theory of continuous creation, which has quite different implications, but before I do that I want to consider this problem of the beginning which is inherent in the evolutionary theories. With an effort of imagination the human mind can trace its way back through the thousands of millions of years of time and space, and we can attempt to describe in common concepts the condition of the primeval atom. The primeval atom was unstable and must have disintegrated as soon as it came into existence. There we reach the great barrier of thought because we begin to struggle with the concepts of time and space before they existed in terms of our everyday experience. I feel as though I've suddenly driven into a great fog barrier where the familiar world has disappeared.

I think one can say that philosophically the essential problem in the conception of the beginning of the universe is the transfer from the state of indeterminacy to the condition of determinacy, after the beginning of space and time when the macrosopic laws of physics apply. When viewed in this way we see that the problem bears a remarkable similarity to one with which we are familiar. This is the indeterminacy which the quantum theory of physics introduces into the behaviour of individual atoms, compared with the determinacy which exists in events where large numbers of atoms are involved. The process of thought by which we reduce the multiplicity of the entire universe to its singular condition of the primeval atom is equivalent in principle to the reduction of the chair in which you are sitting to one of its individual atoms. Not in the evolutionary sense of course, but in the sense that quantum theory and the principle of uncertainty explains why the behaviour of the individual atom is indeterminate and why it is impossible for you to find out the condition of the atom with any precision, because you will disturb it in the very process of investigation. In fact, the application of the fundamental concepts of quantum theory to the cosmological problem enables us to begin the struggle with the barrier which arises whenever we think about the beginning of space and time.

The primeval atom was a singular state of the universe, as incapable of precise specification by physical methods as the familiar individual particle in the uncertainty principle of modern physics. When the primeval atom disintegrated the state of multiplicity set in and the universe became determinate in a macroscopic sense. Philosophically, space and time had a natural beginning when the condition of multiplicity occurred, but the beginning itself is quite inaccessible. In fact, in the beginning the entire universe of the primeval atom was effectively a single quantum unit in the sense that only one of the future innumerable potential states existed. I am aware that this discussion is merely a line of metaphysical thought. Its importance lies in the parallel with the fundamental difficulties and basic indeterminacies in modern quantum theory. If future advances should occur in these directions, then it may become possible to speak with more certainty about the condition of the original cosmological quantum. In the light of our present knowledge of atomic physics it is possible only to surmise the kind of condition which might have existed. I suggested earlier that the density of matter in this primeval atom was inconceivably high. This is arrived at by a simple arithmetical deduction from the probable total mass of the universe as we see it now, and by assuming that the radius of the primeval atom was not greater than, say, a few million miles. However, it is possible that the primeval atom was not like this, but that it consisted of intense radiation and corpuscular rays which formed the primeval gas during the first phases of the expansion. In fact, it is a fundamental concept of Lemaître's theory that the cosmic radiation which we observe today is a relic of this early state. A characteristic of this picture of evolution is the long time-scale involved in the transformation of the intense energy of the original primeval atom, first into the gaseous clouds of hydrogen and then by processes, which awaited the high temperatures and pressures which arose when stars began to form, into the other elements with which we are familiar today. If pressed to describe this primeval atom in conventional terms one would, I think, refer to a gigantic neutron. By radioactive decay this neutron suffered a tremendous explosion. Protons, electrons, alpha particles, and other fundamental particles emerged from it at great velocity and continued to fill all space nearly uniformly as this basic material expanded for many thousands of millions of years until the clusters of galaxies began to form.

An alternative picture of the condition of the primeval atom has been given by Gamov, who believes that it consisted entirely of high-temperature thermal radiation. Five minutes after the expansion began the temperature of the universe was a thousand million degrees, after a day it had fallen to forty million degrees—say, nearly to the temperature of the centre of the sun; after ten million years it had fallen to an average temperature, which we call room temperature. On this theory of Gamov all the chemical elements which we deal with today must have been formed within the first thirty minutes of the life of the universe.

Gamov differs from Lemaître in other important respects. In Lemaître's theory the force of the initial disintegration was exhausted after a few thousand million years, and the expansion which we witness today came into play only as a result of the forces of cosmical repulsion which developed when the galaxies began to form. In Gamov's theory the force of the initial explosion was so great that the expansion of the universe is attained without invoking the force of cosmical repulsion. In other words, the beginning in the Gamov theory is close to the nine thousand million years which we deduce by tracing back the history of the galaxies, and there is no protracted period in the state of diffuse gas with all the major forces balanced as in Lemaître's theory.

The most distinguished living exponent of the evolutionary theory of the origin of the universe is himself in Holy Orders. For him and for all who associate their universe with God, the creation of the primeval atom was a divine act outside the limits of scientific knowledge and indeed of scientific investigation. The probable condition of intense radiation in the primeval atom is entirely consistent with the divine command 'Let there be light'. It would, of course, be wrong of me to suggest that this view of the origin of the universe demands necessarily the possibility of creation of matter by a divine act. On the contrary, those who reject God adopt a strictly materialistic attitude to the problem of the creation of the primeval atom. They would argue that the creation of the primeval material had no explanation within the framework of contemporary scientific knowledge, but would escape from the dilemma by reserving the possibility that science would, if given the opportunity of studying these initial conditions, find a satisfactory solution. Or they would evade the problem of a beginning altogether by following a further line of thought due to Gamov that the primeval atom was not the beginning, but merely a state of maximum contraction of a universe which had previously existed for an eternity of time. I think, however, that for theology, there is one important observation to make. If the universe was created and evolved in the manner just described, then the conception that the creation of the primeval material was a divine act can never be attacked by scientific investigation. A set of conditions which existed over twenty thousand million years ago, and which can never return again, is for ever beyond investigation.

The theory which we have discussed envisages a once

for all creation in the remote past followed by a steady evolution to the present conditions. The alternative to this theory is that the creation of matter is taking place continuously and that although stars and galaxies evolve from this basic material, the universe, when considered as a large-scale structure, is in a steady state. We can illustrate this view by considering the future history of the galaxies which are now near the limit of observation. We are receding at great speed from these galaxies. In a billion years' time the galaxies will have passed for ever from our field of view and other galaxies which are now closer to us will have moved out to our observable horizon. So much is common ground on both the evolutionary and steady-state theories. The sharp distinction arises when we compare the picture of the universe within the observable horizon now and in a billion years' time. On the evolutionary theory more and more galaxies move out of our field of view, and the number of galaxies which we can see with our instruments will for ever decrease. In other words, the average spatial density of the universe is decreasing. On the steady-state theory this is not the case. Although individual galaxies recede beyond the observable horizon, others are always being created to take their place. In a billion years' time the universe will look to us very much as it does now. The individual galaxies will have changed, but their average spatial density remains the same, because matter is always in creation throughout all of space. The cosmological principle of the evolutionary theory in which the universe would appear to be the same to any observer, wherever he was situated in space, has become the perfect cosmological principle according to which the universe is the same throughout all space and time.

The implications of this point of view are, of course, profound. For example, there cannot have been a beginning in any scale of time at all. If we trace back in time the history of the galaxies, they dissolve into gas and then into uncreated matter as they move in towards us, whereas others come into view from beyond the observable horizon. At a time of twenty thousand million years ago the evolutionary models picture the universe as a concentrated conglomerate of gas, whereas the steady-state universe would have appeared as it does today. Indeed, however far we go back in time, there is no stage at which we can say that the universe, as a whole, had a beginning. In the only language at our command we can say that the history of the universe on the steady-state theory extends to an infinite time in the past.

Whereas there is hope that we can put our inferences about the past to an experimental test, we can discuss the future only in terms of the predictions of cosmological theory. Here again there are great differences between the evolutionary and steady-state models. The predictions of the steady-state theory are quite clear.

The universe has an infinite extent in space and an infinite future in time. There is, of course, a limit to the observable universe from any one place in it determined by the speed of expansion. But if an intelligent being exists at our observable limit he would find himself surrounded by a similar universe of galaxies and so on without end. Neither does the theory of continuous creation place any limitation on the future extent in time. In the same way that a billion years ago the universe would look the same as it does now, so in a billion years of future existence the overall large-scale picture will be unchanged.

The future on the evolutionary models is quite different. The total content of matter was fixed once and for all at the time of creation. The expansion is thinning out the galaxies, and in a billion years our view of space would indeed be vastly different from what it is today. In some variations of the evolutionary theory the process of expansion is expected to reverse when the spatial density has fallen to a certain value, and then the contraction of space would bring the ageing galaxies into view again. But even in such variations of the evolutionary models the ultimate death of the universe seems inescapable, because the energy with which the universe was imbued at its creation is relentlessly becoming less available.

The finite limitations of space, time, and content in some of the evolutionary models lead one to ask whether our universe is, in fact, the entire cosmos. It is a question which at present cannot be discussed with profit. There is no feature of the theory which would preclude the existence of other universes created at different times, but unless we are hopelessly wrong in our interpretation of our observations of the universe we see, there is no conceivable way in which we can ever penetrate the regions of time and space where they might exist.

The conflict between the steady-state and evolutionary theories is of the very greatest significance to cosmology and to human thought. The evolutionary theory places the creation of matter at a definite moment in the remote past, beyond human investigation. Although the steady-state theory has no solution to the problem of the creation of matter, it is important to appreciate that if this theory is correct, then the primeval gas is being created now, at this moment, and hence is open to human investigation. On the whole, I think it must be incontestable that the steady-state theory is more materialistic than the evolutionary theory. It could be said that the creation process is a divine act which is proceeding continuously, and which is beyond the conception of the human mind. On the other hand, it cannot be denied that this may be a somewhat perilous attitude for the simple reason that the tools of science can probe the regions of space where this creation is occurring. In fact, in the equations of the cosmologists a creation term already exists. Philosophically, it is, I think, important to emphasize the approachability of the creation of hydrogen which is inherent in these modern theories of continuous creation. Otherwise the metaphysical impact would not be severe. In this sense the concept was stated long ago by Kant in these words '. . . the remaining part of the succession of eternity is always infinite', he said, 'and that which has flowed is finite, the sphere of developed nature is always but an infinitely small part of that totality which has the seed of future worlds in itself, and which strives to evolve itself out of the crude state of chaos through longer or shorter periods. The creation', he went on, 'is never finished or complete. It has, indeed, once begun, but it will never cease.' But, of course, Kant's doctrine was egocentric, in the sense that God had completed the creation in the part of the cosmos which we can see. In the contemporary theories of continuous creation the processes of formation should still be occurring all around us, and are therefore open to human investigation.

I think it is true to say that during the last few years the cosmological issue has crystallized into a conflict between these evolutionary and steady-state theories of the origin of the universe. The variations in detail within these two broad principles are numerous. Many of these differences are highly abstract, but in so far as the stream of human thought is concerned these internal variations are of small consequence compared with the major issue as to whether creation is occurring now and throughout all time in the past and in the future, or whether the fundamental material of the universe was created in its entirety some billions of years ago.

It seems possible that we may be on the verge of settling by experimental observation which of these two principles is correct. In fact, the group of young cosmologists who have promulgated the theories of continuous creation have always emphasized that, as distinct from the theoretical arguments which have surrounded the variations of evolutionary cosmology in the last thirty years, the new theories should be capable of direct experimental test. For example, if with our telescopes we could penetrate so far into space that we could see a cluster of galaxies from which the light had taken nine thousand million years to reach us, then it would be possible to reach a clear decision. For at that time in the past on the evolutionary theory the clusters of galaxies were only just beginning to form from the primeval gas. Well, of course, such a straightforward observation is impossible because of the limited range of our telescopes. I said earlier that the most distant object yet identified in the telescopes is the cluster of galaxies in Hydra at about two thousand million light years. Although the light from this cluster has been travelling through space for two thousand million years, it is too close to us in time and space to be of use in distinguishing between the two theories.

It is, however, on the verge of the regions of space and time where the universe would be expected to be significantly different if creation was still in progress compared with the conditions in an evolutionary universe. If time and space had a beginning, then when the universe was only a few thousand million years old it would be much more compact than it is today. The galaxies would be in existence, but they would be packed closer together compared with their spatial density today. The spatial density today—by which I mean the number of galaxies within, say, fifty or a hundred million light years of the Milky Way—can be determined by the large telescopes. If we could count the number in a similar volume of space at a distance of several thousand million light years we should in effect be making a count of the galaxies as they existed several thousand million years ago. If creation is still taking place, then on the steady-state theories this number should be the same as today. If the evolutionary model is correct, then the spatial density at this distance in time and space will be much greater.

The possibility of carrying out this decisive observational test excites the imagination. Unfortunately it seems likely that the hindrances introduced by the atmosphere of the earth will prevent the great optical telescopes from penetrating to the required regions of space. It may well be that only when optical telescopes can be carried in earth satellites or erected on the moon will it be possible to look back into the past to this extent. Before the advent of such futuristic enterprises it seems likely that the great radio telescopes will give us the answer we require. You may remember that in a previous talk I referred to the collisions of galaxies which, for reasons not yet understood, generate radio waves which can easily be picked up in the radio telescopes, although the light from these galaxies is so faint that they are near the limit of the normally observable universe. We can already study galaxies in collision at such distances that they must be far beyond the range of the optical telescopes. We believe that these investigations are already taking us so far out in space and so far back in time that the radio waves have been on their journey for a few thousand million years. The circumstantial evidence for this belief in the origin of many of the unidentified radio sources is very strong, and if this is confirmed we have the tools with which human beings can bring the cosmological issues to a decisive test.

The concept of continuous creation also presents us with another opportunity to make an even more direct and decisive test. If the theory is correct, then the hydrogen gas which forms the primeval material of the galaxies must be in creation at a considerable rate. The theory demands the appearance of hydrogen at the rate of several billion trillion tons per second in the observable universe. Although this figure is vast, in fact, by ordinary human concepts of terrestrial space the rate is exceedingly slow. It represents the creation of only a few atoms of hydrogen per cubic mile of space per year. The presence of this hydrogen in intergalactic space may well be detectable in the near future by the radio telescopes.

As individuals we must therefore face the possibility that within the next few years astronomers may be able to speak with unanimity about the ultimate cosmological problem. Only the materialist can turn aside unmoved by this prospect. For others, a settlement of this cosmological issue might mean an affirmation or rejection of deeply embedded philosophical and theological beliefs.

So far I have tried to present the contemporary background without prejudice, but no doubt before I finish you will expect me to say a word about my own personal views. At the moment our outlook in astronomy is optimistic. A new epoch has been opened by the development of radio telescopes, and we are perhaps within a generation of an even more astonishing one because of the inherent possibilities of astronomical observations from earth satellites or the moon. We can only guess as to the nature of the remote regions which might be photographed by telescopes removed from their earth-bound environment. In the case of radio telescopes this development is still very young. Three hundred years elapsed between Galileo's small telescope and the inauguration of the 200-inch telescope on Palomar Mountain. In the development of radio telescopes we have not covered a tenth of that time-span. I think therefore that our present optimism may well be of the kind which comes from the initial deployment of great new instruments and techniques. I have no doubt that within a few years these instruments will enable us to resolve the conflict which I have described between the evolutionary and steady-state models. In this process new difficulties will certainly appear, and these might make my present description of the universe as out of date as the static egocentric description which was in vogue in the first twenty years of this century. When we are dealing with time-spans of thousands of millions of years it would be sheer impudence to suggest that the views of the cosmos which have evolved from the techniques developed in our age possess any degree of finality. My present attitude to the scientific aspects of the problem is therefore neutral in the sense that I do not believe that there yet exist any observational data which are decisively in favour of any particular contemporary cosmology. The optimism with which I believe that we are on the verge of producing the necessary observational data is tempered with a deep apprehension, born of bitter experience, that the decisive experiment nearly always extends one's horizon into regions of new doubts and difficulties.

On the question of the creation of the primeval material of the universe it seems to me unlikely that there can ever be a scientific description, whether in terms of the evolutionary or steady-state theories. If the idea of continuous creation is substantiated, then science will have penetrated very far indeed into the ultimate processes of the universe. It might then appear that a completely materialistic framework would have been established, but it does not seem to me that this is the case. If one imagines a scientific device which is so perfect that it could record the appearance of a single hydrogen atom as demanded by the continuous creation theory, then the scientific description of the process would still be imperfect. The same basic and quite fundamental difficulty would appear, as I have described in the case of the primeval atom, in the further effort to obtain information about the nature of the energy input which gave rise to the created atom.

If I were pressed on this problem of creation I would say, therefore, that any cosmology must eventually move over into metaphysics for reasons which are inherent in modern scientific theory. The epoch of this transfer may be now and at all future time, or it may have been twenty thousand million years ago. In respect of creation the most that we can hope from our future scientific observations is a precise determination of this epoch. I must emphasize that this is a personal view.

The attitudes of my professional colleagues to this problem would be varied. Some would no doubt approve of this or a similar line of metaphysical thought. Others would not be willing to face even this fundamental limit to scientific knowledge, although, as I have said, an analogous limitation occurs in modern scientific theory which describes the well-known processes of atomic behaviour. Some, I am afraid, will be aghast at my temerity in discussing the issues at all. As far as this group is concerned, all that I say is that I sometimes envy their ability to evade by neglect such a problem which can tear the individual's mind asunder.

On the question of the validity of combining a metaphysical and physical process as a description of creation, this, as I said earlier, is the individual's problem. In my own case, I have lived my days as a scientist, but science has never claimed the whole of my existence. Some, at least, of the influence of my upbringing and environment has survived the conflict, so that I find no difficulty in accepting this conclusion. I am certainly not competent to discuss this problem of knowledge outside that acquired by my scientific tools, and my outlook is essentially a simple one. Simple in the sense that I am no more surprised or distressed at the limitation of science when faced with this great problem of creation that I am at the limitation of the spectroscope in describing the radiance of a sunset or at the theory of counterpoint in describing the beauty of a fugue.

When I began my talks I mentioned the mixture of fear and humility with which I approached the task. Now you see the irony of the modern astronomer's life in its entirety. The devices of a world war have been forged, with the help of the fear of another, into a system of scientific experiments which take us back through time and space to deal with the problems of the origin of the universe.